THE
Silver Donkey

Joan Morey

The Shepshed Knight Printing Service Limited
91 Charnwood Road, Shepshed, Loughborough, Leics. LE12 9NL

www.shepshedknight.co.uk

First published in Great Britain by
The Shepshed Knight Printing Service Limited 2006

ISBN-13 978-0-9553337-0-5
ISBN-10 0-9553337-0-9

Joan Morey asserts the moral right to
be identified as the author of this work

Set in ITC Giovanni by
The Shepshed Knight Printing Service Limited

Printed and bound in Great Britain by
The Shepshed Knight Printing Service Limited

For Deborah, Carol, Julie, Sarah and Kathryn

FORWARD

I wrote this book, not only for my Great Grandmother Jessica Maria Collins, but also for my children who I love very dearly. I feel that it is important for people to have a history, for my family where it is possible to be able to identify those people.

I want to show how ordinary, everyday people lived during the time of the book. Not everyone had either the money or the freedom to discover their world and their country in ways others, with a little more money could do.

The family members have their actual names, a great many incidents within this story are as have been told to be me by grandmother Lillian Collins, and by my mother Lillian Florence Vesty.

This is the story of real people in real situations, their lives were lived, as those of many others from day to day. They managed their personal finances in a way we today find extraordinary.

At the age of 7 years I can remember the excitement of having electricity, in the way of lighting fitted downstairs. Prior to the coming of electricity to Judges Street the main lighting was gas light. At about the same age I remember the fitting of a flush toilet, prior to this a man with a horse and cart drove around the streets exchanging a full bin for a clean one. This did not only happen in Victorian times. The pump in the garden was where most of the water was withdrawn. There was also a small pump in the scullery, both had to be primed before water was forthcoming.

Life was hard, life was improving but the improvement was slow to reach the working class people in small towns.

Be thankful, today we have so very much. Today our lives are easier and believe it or not we are, in general , more content, A great many of us today can travel where we wish, many have jobs that pay well. We do have pressures some of these very often brought about by the advertising and a way of life depicted as perfect in our eyes. Many are prepared to work and save, or indeed to pay by instalments to get the possessions which may help achieve their dream.

Are we happier? That's up to you to decide.

Joan Morey Loughborough 2006

Jessica Maria Collins

CHAPTER 1

The beginning

The first frost was on the ground, everywhere one looked was white and crisp. Jessica had awoken early, it was cold, she pulled the covers of the bed around her, but felt a tug as her elder sister tugged the covers back.

'Stop it Jess' 'it's freezing'

It was November 15th 1877, little Jessica Maria Jimson had been born eleven years earlier. 'It's my birthday' she exclaimed with obvious delight, she sat up in bed, pulled her knitted shawl around her and hugged her body tightly as if the protect herself with love and cuddles against the cold morning.

Jessica slipped out of bed and scratched away at the frost on the window to look out. The fields opposite the tiny house were blanketed in white. The trees hung heavy with frost, there was a strange silence around as if the birds had overslept, pulling their tiny wings around their bodies to keep in the warmth.

The day proved in the beginning to be nothing special, as Jessica went downstairs, her mother, who had risen an hour earlier had a fire in the grate and the air smelled of wood smoke and boiling, soapy water. Bad weather or not, the washing still had to be done, it was after all Monday.

Her mother passed on her good wishes, she gave Jessica a round of toast from bread freshly made the previous day.

Don't be late for school, there's learning to be done, you need to get better than I have out of life' Jessica's mother explained.

School was not far away, but Jessica knew that her boots leaked, and her stocking had no toes, they had long since become too small for her growing feet, and as the holes in the toes grew progressively larger most of her foot now remained uncovered. Her boots were black, laced and pinched her toes, Jessica considered these were small problems, as at least she still had both parents and a loving family to take care of her. Some of her school friends had lost either mothers or fathers by the time they were her age.

As the days grow cold, the spider webs become heavy with the dew of the day. It is at this time of the year that many children, would make fairy mirrors on their way to and from school. The leaves are stripped from a twig, which is then bent into a circular shape. The trick is to catch the web of the spider, without the spider being an attachment. The dew still hanging heavily on the translucent cords which make up one of heavens miracles. Water is now necessary, if there isn't a small puddle, or any water close by then the experiment is a failure. The hoop of the twig is very gently placed in the water and it is at this very precise moment, when the spider web, laden with dew, scoops up more water and becomes a mirror to rival any that Titania would use. It was such a game that Jessica and her friends frequently played on their way to school, but this morning the frost was too heavy and their interest lay in getting warm.

The journey to school held no surprises, she had met some of the others on her journey. They chatted, they clung to each other, as though they were old married couples, huddled closely together for extra warmth, their breath spilling out in a constant stream of mist as the warmth from their bodies mixed with the cold of the early morning air.

In the foreground of the school the children gathered. Miss Parkin came out huddled in a thick shawl and quickly rang the little hand-bell that was to summon them to their class.

The twenty or so children aged between five years and eleven stopped their chatter immediately. The air hung with silence and expectancy. Like a pendulum of a clock stopped mid flow the children lined up, and marched in silence into the school, swinging their arms to and fro across their bodies.

Their teacher Miss Parkin had risen early from her school house adjoining the small school and lit the fire to give welcoming heat to the classroom. As normal at this time of year, the daily routine began with the children standing in rows behind their desks awaiting Miss Parkins instructions.

'Cup your hands, blow on your fingers', they need this, the early frost had really penetrated their fragile young skins this cold morning.

'Stamp your feet, swing your arms', the instructions continued in this mode, until the faces were glowing with warmth and the young students were looking relaxed and ready to begin their work. They knew Miss Parkin hadn't failed them. Fresh oatcakes would be the order of the day. This feast of oatcakes wasn't a regular occurrence, but on cold days, birthdays, or special anniversaries Miss Parkin always provided her charges with a little treat of somekind or another. The food, was given by the owners of the Hall, but Miss Parkin, was responsible for the cooking, and for the general education of the children.

All the children belonged to the poor families who lived in the cottages belonging to the Hall. The hall was owned by a family, who had made their fortune in banking, and who were fortunately reasonably fair employers and landlords.

'Good morning children, today is a special day for Jessica Jimson. She is celebrating her birthday, and on this frosty morning, I've provided a dish of oatcakes to get you nice and warm before we start work.'

The children clapped their hands to applaud Jessica's birthday, and as they did every morning, stood to attention in rows until given permission to sit. Miss Parkin announced that the hymn of praise might be very appropriate today, and led the children in a slightly out of season , but still rousing rendition of 'Good Christian Men Rejoice', after all it was getting near to Christmas.

Jessica did struggle with the concept of addition and subtraction and never could at her tender age, understand why she should be required to work in pounds, shillings and pence when for the life of her she would not see a time when she would need to calculate such vast sums of money. The kind of calculations she was being required to perform would be fine for the rich people, those who manipulated the daily lives of the poorer sections of society.

The children studied the vast continent of Africa where people with many differing shades of skin inhabited. She learned about the peoples of the Bible. Those from the romantic sounding countries such as Ethiopia, Arabia, Egypt with whom she had met in her dreams, after reading the Old Testament. She imagined their clothes, pictured the colours.

She had seen the illustrations in some Bibles and never for one moment had thought that fashions could possibly have changed in these far away lands. Jessica still thought of Egypt as the place of the Pharaohs', the place where, all those years ago Moses had led his people through the desert, across the Red Sea to freedom. So much information, Miss Parkin must be oh so very clever to be able not only to retain this knowledge, but also to impart it to her pupils.

There was work at different stages being taught. The older pupils helping out for at least one hour during each day in the education of the younger ones. In the afternoon for the girls the daily routine was one of housecraft. This consisted in the main of mending and finishing. The housekeeper at the hall would send down a weekly basket of mending which the girls would undertake. The more complex and difficult tasks allocated to the older children, the button sewing and light running stitches to the younger of her pupils. Work of this kind supplemented the finances of the school and helped to keep the children catered for by means of extra books, chalks etc. At 4pm school finished, the children left the school in a noisy rabble, eager to get home, particularly on a cold winters day. They would leave as if they were a crowd of young puppies let out for a quick romp away from their mother, tumbling and tripping over each other in their eagerness to be away and free from the restrictions of their daily learning.

The majority of the students lived nearby, the small gathering of houses were mostly owned by the Squire of the hall, most of their parents worked in some capacity or other at the hall. Jessica reached home, her step still light, after all it was her birthday, wasn't it? She pushed open the creaking wooden door. A door which had been creaking open daily for the best part of a hundred years. The paint had long

5

since faded and cracked, leaving the wood exposed to the elements. Wood that had once been a vibrant living thing was now dead and dried. There were occasions when Jessica need to give the door an extra push, as the rags which hung on the inside of the door frequently got jammed in the hinge this made the door very difficult to open. The rags were there for a very good reason. The door had, after so many years, cracked and left gaps, open to the cold air. During those cold damp winters the rags hung over the door, placed in order to make an attempt to keep out the continual draughts, which, affected her mothers rheumatism, causing swelling and pain to her joints. Years of working on a damp stone floor had caused her feet to become cracked and painful, especially when she had placed them close to the fire to warm a little.

The kitchen was inviting with the smell of freshly baked bread, and potatoes baking in their jackets. Mother had saved a little of the rice she'd bought on her last trip to the town, and made a luxurious milky rice pudding. No one, either castle, palace, hall or great mansion could ever have hoped for a better rice pudding than that baked by mother, especially when dusted sparingly with a little nutmeg, as extra treat.

The family ate heartily, when they had finished Jessica helped her mother to wash the plates, they chatted about the day, her mother was just about to begin a discussion with Jessica.

"Jess, your now eleven and...'

An argument in the background prevented further discussion. The two younger boys had begun an argument and this required sorting before Jessica's father became involved and the culmination of any argument in the household ended in a slap.

Jessica hurried to find just what the boys had fallen out

over. Thomas, who was eight had wanted to draw on an old poster, the poster had fallen, or had been taken from a tree, but Jim who was seven had decided he would also like to draw; of course on the same piece of paper. Jessica suggested that the best solution to the argument and to a quieter evening was for them both to go to bed. After she had explained that anyway there was just enough oil to last for two more days and everyone would shortly be in bed, there was no contesting they calmed down and trudged upstairs.

After peace had been restored, Jessica's mother and father sat in their respective chairs on either side of the fireplace, gathering the last warmth from the dying embers, whilst the oil lamp burned its sallow glow which cast shadows around the room.

A stone sink lay under the window, water being provided from the well in the back yard. A sturdy oak table stood in the centre of the room with two roughly hewn benches either side of the table. A wooden rocking chair, which was made as a wedding present for Jessica's mother by her father took pride of place to the right of the fireplace. The positioning of the chair almost blocked off the door to the steep staircase. The fireplace was a wide mouthed space with a gridiron to hold the large iron kettle, and an old wooden cupboard that had one leg broken, where the rot of ages had taken its toll. Jessica's father simply never found the time to fashion another leg, instead a block of wood held the cupboard upright, although he was perfectly capable of doing so, of late he appeared so very tired when he came in from a days work.

Jessica rose to say goodnight to her parents. She bent to kiss her mother, who held her hand and stroked it gently before announcing,

'no school for you tomorrow dear, you're to be up at the

hall at 8 O'clock sharp, if they approve of you you'll be starting work shortly and living in, but you'll come home regularly so don't worry'

The shock was enormous for Jessica, in her heart she already knew that this would be the pattern of her life, but she had pushed the idea to the back of her mind hoping the inevitable would never happen.

She went to bed without another word, but as she climbed onto the stiff horsehair mattress next to her sister who had retired earlier, the tears welled up in Jessica's eyes and she cried herself to sleep.

That night she slept fitfully. Her dreams were ones of being lost in a vast mansion. Of rooms so numerous there was no escape. Of shouting for someone to come to her aid, but no one ever did. Of cold, extreme cold, the kind of cold in winter which enters your very bones, which chills you through so that you simply fail in being able to stop your teeth from chattering. Would she escape? Would she find her way home? Would she survive?

CHAPTER 2

Jessica awoke to her mother calling her from downstairs. She quickly washed in the small bowl of water, but not before breaking the ice. She dried herself of the cloth on the small dresser and put on her shabby black alpaca dress. The dress had once belonged to one of the daughters of the Squire Port-Clements, and had been passed by the Governess to Jessica's father, the dress had been worn by Jessica's sisters, Emma and Polly. Emma and Polly were already in service in big houses in the nearby town. Loughborough was about five miles away, but unless they could get a lift in the hall delivery cart which went to the market the ancient market was held in the town centre on a Thursday or Saturday, plus it coincided with theirs days off, visiting was very difficult. At least, thought Jessica, I'm only working across the road, only ten minutes walk from home, so visiting mother would not really pose too much of a problem.

Tom worked as a farm hand on the estate, and it was for this reason that Jessica had been given a trial placement at the hall. Jessica's father was a well built, ruddy faced man.

9

His once curly hair was now thinning and stuck out at strange angles across his head. It did not help matters that he was prone to constantly run his fingers through his remaining hair which had the effect of not only making it stand on end, but also of producing static electricity which made it appear to spring into a life of its own. Tom, her father was also apt to have strange twitches and at times would fall to the ground, shaking uncontrollably. Family, friends and work colleagues alike knew of this problem and would stay by Tom as his rode out his storm. When he awoke, he rarely knew anything of the past minutes but would be very tired and have trouble in walking.

'Right gel' said her father,' let's make a start then'

'Bye Mam', said Jessica

'See you soon gel, behave and don't get into any trouble,' said her much saddened mother.

The driveway of the hall was bounded at the roadside by two large stone gate-posts, and an enormous pair of wrought iron gates. Although Jessica had always lived within sight of them, she paused, looking up at the large imposing gateway, with the gates now standing open. Her father gripped her hand re-assuringly. She looked up at him, and he smiled gently down at her. The driveway was long and winding, about halfway along this drive, was the church where the family were obliged to worship every Sunday, along with the entire company of estate workers. It had been the church where Jessica's mother and father had been married, and where Jessica, along with all her siblings had been christened. Jessica looked at the church, with its little graveyard, and tombs dedicated to the members of the Port-Clements family, long deceased, and wondered at the Sermon preached by the vicar only two days before, entitled 'Behold I will make you all free, for I am the fisher of men' Why then, she thought am I now only the day after my birthday to be put to work and as far as I can think, I've not got any freedom?

CHAPTER 3

The head gardener was discussing the planting of a new crop with the under gardeners as they passed. As with all under employees Tom doffed his cap and wished his 'good morning'.

'Good morning Mr. Paget'

'Good morning to you Tom' said the man with the deep voice.

Jessica imagined him shouting and bellowing his orders, perhaps that was why his voice seemed so sonorous. Jessica was shivering in the cold November sunlight

'I'd best be going now, my girls' got a job up at the hall', said her father

'Ay, best not be late, thou knows what hers like' answered the gardener.

'Cum on gel', said Tom attempting to sound cheery.

Jessica nodded in agreement, and pulled the coarse woollen shawl tightly around her shoulders.

They continued on their way along the long driveway. Every step became a painful reminder of the day before when she was a carefree young child attending the village school.

At last the kitchen door was reached, her father knocked

timidly and waited. Again he knocked, perhaps they hadn't heard his first one, after-all the door was very heavy.

The door, was eventually pulled open by a young girl not much older than Jessica herself. She wore a black dress, over which she wore an apron made from stiff sacking. Her hands were dirty, and as she peered around the door, she wiped her nose with the back of her hand and dragged it down the apron, sniffed, and eventually said:

"Hello you the new girl, come in she's waiting for you"

Jessica was aware of her father squeezing her hand, and she looked up into his kindly brown eyes. He gave her a reassuring nod, and gently pushed her forward through the half open door.

Jessica found that the temperature inside the bare corridor appeared no warmer than the frosty environment outside. Again she shivered and whispered,

"Dad I'm scared" Her father squeezed her and once again, but this time held himself erect and stared straight ahead.

Liza, the girl who had opened the door walked up the cold servants corridors, whilst at the same time chattering about the fact that Jessica would now thankfully be taking over the cleaning of brass throughout the house. Explaining that she would now be the one in trouble should the brass not have a mirror like finish.

After what seemed to Jessica to be an interminable journey down faceless corridors they arrived at the door that lead into the large kitchen. The door was tightly closed, and the only sound to be heard was the rasping noise produced by someone on the kitchen side scrubbing the floor.

Liza knocked timidly at the door and gently pushed it open.

"Mind that your feet a clean", came a brusque voice.

CHAPTER 4

Feet were wiped vigorously on the rough mat before they stepped into the large expanse.

The kitchen was warm. A variety of smells pervaded the air, the smell of pastry being baked, of potato peelings, of greens being prepared for the evening meal. There was a clamour and clatter from the servants busy on their various jobs and the pans being knocked against one another, either in the process of washing and cleaning or of the placing upon the numerous hooks. Copper pans gleamed in the light given off from the open fire of the kitchen range. It's front having been dropped to provide more warmth on this cold frosty day.

A high shelf encompassed the kitchen bedecked with a selection of colourful plates and above all this the statutory painted sign of 'Waste not want not', which appeared to obligatory in every large country house kitchen. A warning to the servants that waste used money and money equalled good health and payment for their services.

A large table stood in the centre of the room, the pine gleaming having recently been scrubbed. The grain still showing rough after its' soaking. The table had probably stood in the same place for in excess of a hundred years and was still weathering the test of time.

A low stone sink has been placed against a wall a sink of a buff coloured glaze that was popular for all around this time. The sink was very shallow with a hand pump by its side to provide ice -cold water for the preparation of vegetables. The whole assembly stood on a roughly made brick plinth.

Another sink, this time made from lead stood a few feet away.

The black range was highly polished with black leading applied daily before the fire was well alight. The ovens within the range cleaned out regularly. Taking pride of place before the range was a rocking chair and before the chair, laid out on the floor a new made hand pegged and brightly coloured rug. A large wicker basket stood by the stove filled with logs.

Near the door which Jessica was later to discover lead to the serving hall, and then onto the dining hall, was a young girl. The girl was dressed in a brown dress, with a sacking bag tied around her waist. She was rhythmically scrubbing the floor in circular movements, occasionally dipping the brush, almost too large for her small hands into a large galvanised bucket. The girls' hands were red, and Jessica judged by the amount of steam rising from the bucket, that the water was hot.

Jessica's father, cap in hand addressed Mrs. Lewis. Mrs. Lewis was the head cook and therefore responsible for the servants working in the kitchen. She had an added responsibility of being in charge of the below stairs servants. Below stairs servants are those who work at the menial tasks performed in the running of a country house. Clearing out the grates, lighting fires, cleaning the pans, scrubbing the floors in the servants area, and generally keeping the dirt from the door were amongst the tasks for these juniors. As a general rule the young below stairs servants would be distinguished by the wearing of brown dress. The sacking covers which they wore were by necessity to keep the majority of dirt away from their clothes, as these were in short supply so keeping them as clean as possible was important.

'Good day missus, this is my girl Jessica', said Mr. Jimson as he gently dislodged Jessica's hand from his and pushed her forward.

The woman was large and ruddy faced. Her grey hair was pinned back and wisps were escaping from beneath her cap. She lifted a hand, and with a soft podgy finger pushed the hair behind her ears. Mrs. Lewis had large grey eyes and a smiling mouth. She must have been a very handsome woman, who even at around forty -five years old was still reasonably attractive. Mrs. Lewis, had, over the past few years become known as a person who was given to sudden changes in temperament. She was of course of an age where women were well known for their troubles.

'Come on gel, lets have a look at you then', she said in a kindly voice.

Jessica's father gave her yet another tender push, and Jessica, eyes cast down to the floor, her upper teeth almost breaking the skin of her lower lip, hands balled so hard her nails cutting into her palms, moved forward to where Mrs. Lewis awaited. Mrs. Lewis, now seated in the huge rocking chair, gently grasped Jessica by the shoulders, and releasing her right hand palm downwards, forefingers extended, tipped Jessica under the chin until Jessica was staring fearfully into Mrs. Lewis' grey eyes.

CHAPTER 5

'You're a fine looking gel, you'll do alright ere, so long as you do what yer told an speak when you're spoken to' Mrs. Lewis said in a matter of fact voice.

'Yes mmm', said Jessica.

'Right then, I'll get Mary to show you where you'll sleep, and to give you your clothes. 'Say goodbye to your dad, you'll see him soon enough' said Mrs. Lewis.

Jessica was unsure whether she was actually permitted to cross the kitchen to give her father a hug. She gazed at him longingly.

'Goodbye Dad, see you soon'

Her father put out his arms and said, with a voice that echoed encouragement and love,

'Come on girl, your not going to prison you know, come an give me a kiss".

Jessica bounded across the kitchen with such eagerness she almost sent poor Mary, who was still gently scrubbing the floor, head first into her bucket of water, as she made a rush into her father's arms. It was at this point that she found she

17

could contain her tears no longer, she bit her lips to attempt to get her emotions under control but it was too late. The floodgates were open, and she could taste the fresh saltiness in her mouth in seconds. Tears streamed down her face dripping off her nose and her chin. She wiped then away with the back of her hand but more came. The sobs followed, rending sobs. Her father held her tight, he enclosed her in his arms light a tight blanket of love. He lifted her face to look at her.

'You're a big girl now, go on with you, I'll see you near every day when I'm working in the garden'.

Mr. Jimson shook the fat hand of Mrs. Lewis and thought to himself how soft they were in comparison to Jess his wife's hands. She'd been making wicker baskets for the head gardener just about all their working lives and her hands were coarse with the unresisting wicker. Now that winter had returned they would be cracked and bleeding. How he wished he could spare her just a few days rest.

Mr. Jimson turned, he walked at a pace much faster than usual and when he reached the back door and opened it and the cold air touched his skin, only then did he allow himself to gently brush away the tears that had begun to wend their way down his craggy face to the curve of his lips. If anyone is looking, he thought, they will think the cold has started me nose running.

Meanwhile, Mrs. Lewis had instructed Mary to wipe her hands, and show Jessica where she would be spending her sleeping hours. As with maids, house maid's, ladies maids, scullery maids of this time most of Jessica's waking hours would be spent working in the kitchen.

The winding corridors that Mary led Jessica along were cold, damp and unwelcoming. The conditions still luxurious compared to Jessica's home, but this wasn't her home, Jessica spoke at last:

" How am I ever going to find my way round, I'll get lost"!

'I'll be with you for a start". Said Mary. We're in the same room, and I'll show you what to do first".

Jessica smiled for the first time since her mother had spoken of her impending change of life, she did feel relieved to know that Mary would be her companion.

They continued on their way to the bedrooms, through old paint crazed doors, up winding narrow staircases. The place where Jessica was to spend the next few years of her life seemed to be totally labyrinthine, and Jessica still had her doubts about even being able to find her way alone, ever.

At last a small door was reached on the upper attic floor, and Mary announced that this was it. Mary twisted the small, loose brass door -knob, the door creaked open Jessica peeped inside. The two girls entered, and Jessica, although she was well wrapped up shivered, as the cold air encircled her. The furnishings were sparse, but solid, in fact, it was far from utilitarian. As time moved on so did the furniture. As the master of the house purchased some new furniture, and because of the way primogenitor existed amongst the serving community, even at the very end of the chain there were benefits.

The beds however, were not in such good condition; they were cots, made up from rough-hewn wood, with mattresses of horsehair. Mary pointed to the cot by the window and indicated that this, small space would be occupied by Jessica. A perfect position in the summer, but, in winter, not by any stretch of the imagination the height of luxury. Jessica walked across the bare floor boards towards the bed, her small hand stroked the covers, how soft, how wonderful, even though there were numerous holes caused by sheer age, they were a far cry from home. Jessica commented on the beauty of those parts of the cover still appearing to be untouched by age, dust of sunlight.

'It's the stuff the house doesn't want any more and Jose, she's the one what just got married, patched the holes with other worn out bits' said Mary.

'Can you just imagine how beautiful it looked once, oh, I'd have curtains to match, and walk around all day just looking if I were a lady'. Jessica said, as she closed her eyes in a dream like trance.

'Well your not' said Mary, jolting her back to reality, 'an if we don't go down right now, Mrs. Lewis'll have us both in the coal ole polishing coal'.

'We don't have to do that as well do we?', asked Jessica, visualising the impossibility of such a task.

CHAPTER 6

J essica soon settled into the routine of the house, and because she was polite and hard working, she very rarely crossed Mrs. Lewis, who in fact became protective of her.

Every second week Jessica was allowed an afternoon free. Immediately after lunch she would hurry down the long drive in order to visit her parents. She would try to ensure that a small gift was available for Tom and Jim, her brothers. She would try, if it were practicable to save her dessert for two meals prior to her visit. Of course, this would depend on its constituency. She would carefully wrap these in a small bag. The bag was a treasure and one of Jessica's only true possessions. Often during that first winter, after all the tasks had been performed to the satisfaction of Mrs. Lewis, Jessica would sit on a small stool next to the rocking chair whilst Mrs. Lewis observed, guided and tutored Jessica in the art of crochet. By mid February Jessica had, to the satisfaction of both parties produced a small bag in which to carry her presents home.

On this still cold mid March day Jessica made her way

home. She reached the cottage where she had spent the first eleven years of her life and pushed open the door. Everywhere was quiet, and the fire had burned very low.

'Mam', called Jessica, but no one answered, 'Mam', strange, she thought, she knew I was coming home, she's always waiting with a good cup of tea, eager to hear my tales of the hall after a further two long weeks away.

Jessica walked out of the house and back towards the road. She began to walk towards the school. Perhaps, she thought her mother had decided to take a stroll to meet the boys from school.

As she rounded the bend, she could see, in the distance a small group of people moving slowly towards her. Suddenly, she didn't feel safe, she didn't feel secure, she didn't feel anything. Why?, why should she feel this way?

The closer the people came to Jessica, the more people she recognised. Her neighbours, friends of her parents, her mother, her head bent, shawl over her head, crying, walking beside a slowly moving horse and cart. Jessica sensed panic, her heart pounded so loudly all other sound was blotted out. Her legs would not move, she tried to call, but no sound would come.

When the cart was level with her it was then she saw her father stretched on the cart, his face almost unrecognisable, a strange bloated shape, eyes staring, and blue, oh how so blue. Jessica ran to her mother's side, and looked into her face, but her mother could utter no sound, she simply showed the look of terrible pain and anguish. Jessica hung around her mother's waist, and both dragged each other along the road.

The men carried her father's body into the house, and set him down in the front room. They touched their forelocks, and walked out without speaking, leaving Jessica and her mother standing in a state of total shock.

Mrs. Lewis was informed, and sent a message that Jessica need not return for one week, until her father had been buried and her mother comforted.

The funeral was quiet and sombre. The carpenter at the Hall made a coffin. Mrs. Moore their neighbour from next door weaved wreaths of flowers of early Spring. The horse and cart drew up at the door and Mr. Jimson's coffin was borne out of the tiny cottage to the awaiting cart by the grooms from the Hall in full livery.

The procession set off for the church in the hall grounds. Emma and Clara had also been given a weeks leave from their jobs and Jessica's house was once again full, but, oh God, how silent, how very silent. Jessica, who was not far out of her eleventh birthday had grown into a responsible young woman in just a few short hours, and being the one who was able to visit her mother more regularly than the others, now felt a sense of great responsibility.

The evening of the funeral, the family sat by the light of a small candle, it was only then, when none could cry any more did Clara eventually break the silence.

'How, Mam, How?' she asked.

Her mother reminded them how their father was sometimes given to strange unaccountable fits. It was whilst out getting watercress for their mother to make into her delicious soup, that their father had suffered another fit. He was alone, and had slipped, face down, and drowned in the shallow stream where that wonderful tasting free food grew so profusely.

'Never again' said their mother, 'never will I use that damnable plant'.

No one ever mentioned the soup made from this plant

again and it was never offered again.

Life settled down once again into a regular pattern. Jessica grew a little older and a little more beautiful each day. Her dark eyes and hair that had a slight curl and wispiness to it, surrounded her round face as a frill around a party dress. She worked very hard, and although the hours were long and arduous she could never actually say she disliked the work.

Mrs. Lewis had taken to her, particularly after the death of her father, making sure that now the bread winner of the house was there no longer the family did not go without.

Each time Jessica went home Mrs. Lewis ensured there was always a cloth on the table for her to take home full of good things to eat, and occasionally clothes which were being discarded by the children of the house, which, to her mother's good fortune seemed always to fit the boys. In addition a little work was provided in the shape of mending work, and because her mother was a fine needlewoman, even replacement napkins were ordered, when old table linen wore out.

CHAPTER 7

L ife settled down to a constant routine of work and visits home. One day on her usual visit at a time when
Jessica was reaching her fourteenth birthday, she asked her
mother for permission to visit the local fair on her next day
off. The fair was held on the nearest Thursday, Friday and
Saturday nearest to Lady-day. This is in November.

The fair always aroused a great deal of excitement at the
hall. Mrs. Lewis went to great pains to work out a rota which
would enable all those interested in a visit to have at least
one evening off during that three day period whereby they
could indeed let their hair down and relax.

'I could meet Emma and Clara, and wouldn't really be
alone, as there will be others from the hall going' said Jessica
persuasively whilst clasping her mother's hands in her own,
now very strong ones.

'And who pray are you going to walk those miles to and fro
with in the dark of winter miss? Asked her mother.

'The cart is going from the hall Mam, there'll be five of us
riding together, and I'll be careful not to speak to anyone I

don't know Mam, honest I will', answered Jessica with excitement in her voice.

'Alright then, but send me a message that you got back safely won't you?'

On Friday the 12th November, Jessica set out, shawl over her head and two pairs of thick stockings to guard against the bitter weather. The sky had hung black all day, and now, as the girls and young men from the hall travelled in the open cart, the first drops of freezing rain began to fall. They huddled closer, and pulled the tarred cloth, used for covering the goods, tightly over their heads and giggled for sheer joy of their adventure.

They reached the town centre, cold, and forlorn, but Jessica soon cheered up as she spotted her sisters' huddled together in Allsops, the drapers doorway. They waved and beckoned her to join them. Jessica ran over to them and clasped their hands amid kisses a cuddles.

'Mam sends her love'. She said, 'an I'm to meet the cart at 9 O'clock.' It was then 6.30pm.

Jessica had never been to the fair before, and had only heard her Uncle talk about it. The day time was always given over to a hiring fair, and he was used to attending each May and November, when he put himself up for hiring.

A hiring fair was a time when, young men, young women and sometimes older ones, who had fallen on really hard times visited the town centre. The local farmers would turn up with their carts and hire casual labour for their farms. The whole area, lived on either manufacturing, especially hosiery or agriculture. In addition to those people wanting employment or to employ there were all kind of stalls selling everything imaginable, but especially at the November fair there would be Geese, spices, fruits and nuts, all the things that make winter and particularly Christmas a slightly more bearable time of year.

Jessica was eager to look around. There was such a cacophony of sound, music, people shouting and selling their wares, singers, vendors of strange things, calling, some trying to entice people to spend a little of their hard earned money in order to buy entry to a tent.

The tents, crudely erected contained many exciting things, things beyond belief. There were strange creatures from far distant lands, women, with beards, so long they could be plaited, men or women, so grossly overweight, they could neither walk nor stand unaided.

All poor people, for whom the miracles of medicine at that time could do no good. They lived their lives as objects of derision, to be stared at and laughed at. Jessica could clearly hear a man who seemed very close to where the small group of sisters were standing, trying to encourage the folk to view, a lady, or a man, he claimed not to know.

'Ladies and Gentlemen, it's a strange twist of nature, it don't even know itself what it is. Come and see for yourself, if you can tell, I'll give you a quid'.

It was raining hard now, but this wasn't going to deter Jessica, the sights, the sounds, the smells, the lights, how she was captivated. She just wanted to drink the whole experience, just as her employers drank best wines from their cellars. The experience for Jessica held more excitement, and was just as intoxicating as the very best wine.

'Cum on I can't miss a thing, it is so wonderful', said Jessica.

Her sisters sighed, they pulled their shawls tightly over their heads and stepped into the rain. Jessica danced from stall to stall gazing at the goods on offer. You could try to knock a coconut off a stand, or throw a ball in the mouth of a Pierot. The Pierot, with his comical clothes, decorated with sequins and pointed hat, sat, with an open mouth, whilst the comical head twisted this way and that on a spindle.

' I'd never do that said Jessica, never in a million years.'

'Why do you think they offer those good prizes'? said Clara, it's because it's practically impossible to win'.

'But that's cheating', said Jessica.

'No it's competition', said Emma.

Jessica looked longingly at a plate with a bouquet of roses painted on it, and wished she had a farthing to spend on this game of chance. Mam would love to own something as beautiful as that, and I would love to give it to her, she thought.

By the time Jessica reached the hall it was 10pm, the lights in the kitchen were burning brightly, and after taking off their wet shawls and shoes, the wet but happy group settled down at the large kitchen table to a warm mug of hot milk and honey which had been prepared for their homecoming.

'I'm having none of my staff falling ill after a night out' stated Mrs. Lewis, 'when you've all finished your drinks tell me about it, then off to bed with you, and no noise, the master an mistress have retired early, they'll be ell to pay if their woke'.

Jessica tip toed into her room, cold but happy. Mary muttered and turned over in bed but didn't wake. That night although weary it took Jessica a while to get to sleep. The sights and sounds seemed to vie for places in her brain, each time she closed her eyes her heart was pounding. She pulled the covers over her ears in order to keep out the draught from the small bedroom window, and eventually fell asleep with a contented smile on her face.

A few days later Mrs. Lewis called Jessica, 'now gel you've

always worked hard and you deserve to see how the other half live'.

She inclined her head towards the door which led into the serving corridors and then to the entrance hall. Jessica fidgeted, wondering what Mrs. Lewis meant. Mrs. Lewis carried on,

'Over there on the back of that chair is a new dress, apron and cap go try them on then come back here in them, so as I can alter em should they need it'.

Jessica still looked puzzled, she then plucked up courage to speak; 'Mrs. Lewis, I don't understand what am I to do, why have I got these clothes?"

'Well', said Mrs. Lewis in a slow drawl, chubby arms folded over her ample bosom, 'you're about to start learning how to set an wait at table, it's getting near Christmas, and you know how they love to entertain. You've been here three years now girl, and have developed into a comely enough being to be acceptable to them'.

'I can't ', exclaimed Jessica, 'I'll spill the food, I know I will, I'm too nervous, I'm shaking now an you've just told me about it, anyway how am I going to speak to them?'

'You don't speak, said Mrs. Lewis sharply, 'you smile, you nod, you shake your head, you do as they say, but you don't speak, not ever. Now away with you and start now to do as you're told. Get that frock tried on, an quick about it, you've got other jobs to do you know, an Miss Pritchard will want to inspect you'. You've got a lot of learning to do over the next few months, you've got to be perfect'.

Miss Pritchard, Jessica hadn't thought of that, if the idea of working in the hall proper had worried Jessica, then the idea of being under the auspice of Miss Pritchard was ten times worse.

Miss Pritchard, was a woman about thirty years old, she was very attractive with beautiful sand coloured hair, drawn sleekly and tightly back into a neat twist plait. Her eyes were the deepest azure blue imaginable. On the brief occasions that Jessica had seen her when she came in to discuss the food. Mrs. Lewis usually went to her room, Jessica had felt that her eyes were like the deepest pools, and she always needed to tell herself that it was rude to stare. Up to now she had managed it and had quickly resumed her work.

Miss Pritchard had high cheekbones, a mouth that showed her gentle nature, and a small pretty nose. Her figure was the talking point amongst most of the female servants. Her dresses always appeared to have been especially moulded to fit her. Her walk was the most graceful anyone could remember. As would be imagined, Miss Pritchard was also the stuff that dreams are made of as far as male personnel were concerned. To Squire Porth-Clements, she was one of the jewels in his collection, but as far as Miss Pritchard was concerned, her value was in her business like running of daily affairs in the hall, and her business like attitude was always with her. Men may look, but men may certainly not touch.

Jessica ran to her room with the new clothes over her arm. She removed her old dress and apron, and standing shivering in the cold she shook out the dress. After a great deal of time, Jessica stood in front of Mrs. Lewis.

'That took some time eh?' the friendly cook laughed.

'Sorry Mrs. Lewis' said Jessica, head lowered, shuffling from one foot to another. 'I can't do all the buttons, I tried, honest, but I just can't reach em all, an I'm sure I'll never be able to tie me apron bow like the others.'

'Come here girl, you look like a bag of rags, such a comely thing can look better than that', Mrs. Lewis grabbed Jessica's arms and began tugging and twisting her dress, spinning her round to fasten buttons and tying her apron. When she was happy that Jessica looked presentable, Mrs. Lewis said;

'Mary, go knock on Miss Pritchard's door, and tell her Jessica's ready for her inspection'.

Miss Pritchard seemingly glided into the kitchen and spoke directly to Jessica.

'Good morning young woman, I believe you're going to learn the techniques of silver service and place setting, followed by the niceties of serving at table'.

Jessica understood not one word, she'd never heard of silver serving, surely they didn't, no but what then? She looked at Miss Pritchard blankly.

'Answer then gel, as the cat got your tongue?' said Mrs. Lewis, with a hint of amusement in her voice.

Jessica of course had thought she was allowed to speak to no one above stairs. She looked at Mrs. Lewis, then across to Miss Pritchard, her blue eyes drawing every word Jessica was attempting to say. Eventually, after much clearing of throat and stuttering Jessica spoke in a nervous whisper.

'I don't know what you're talking about Miss Pritchard, I'm dead scared to go through there', she nodded towards the hall doorway, which lead into the residential area.

'I don't expect you to know now Jessica, you've got five weeks before the first dinner part, you're a bright girl I understand from Mrs. Lewis, and she assures me that you are quite capable of the job'.

Miss Pritchard seemed very calm and indeed quite pleasant, to the contrary of the below stairs gossip.

'Now', she said. 'stand straight and let me see how your dress fits'.

It was Miss Pritchard who pinned the dress, she tugged,

she spun Jessica around, she had her walking up and down until she was quite certain the new uniform looked, or would look impeccable.

'Run off, and quickly change now Jessica, your first lesson will be here in the kitchen', said Miss Pritchard.

Jessica was eager to escape, and set off at a rapid rate until she heard the voice of Mrs. Lewis.

'How longs' it take you to unbutton then eh?'

Jessica stopped in her tracks and returned to the kitchen. 'Silly ha'porth', said Mrs. Lewis, unbuttoning the inaccessible buttons, and tapping Jessica on the shoulders. 'Now don't be long'.

The following afternoon, and every afternoon for the next week Jessica spent in learning everything there was to know about setting a table for a dinner party. Ellen, a young woman of about 28 years was detailed by Miss Pritchard to instruct her. The master and the family had gone to London for the week, in order to pick out new clothes for the coming season so the dining room was not in use. Initially, Jessica used the crockery from the kitchen, as she was nervous and Ellen was afraid that the slightest accident could prove expensive. The silver centrepieces had to be cleaned, the floral decorations adjusted and readjusted, the glassware polished, inspected and polished again. When the light began to fade the candelabra was lit, and Jessica would stand and gaze in absolute wonder. How the silver glistened. How the glassware sparkled. It was like a thousand tiny stars had drifted down from heaven and alighted on the gleaming white damask tablecover.

After Jessica had learned about the table, she began her training on serving food. She learned how to pick up signals on when to move to clear the dishes, replace new ones and to discreetly clear away any spillages without drawing attention to herself or the guest who had a mishap. Jessica had even been presented with what was to become her most prized possession, a mirror. Miss Pritchard gave this to her and said;

'to be presentable is on of the pre-requisites of your job, you must ensure you are a paragon of cleanliness and tidiness before you enter the dining room. Not a speck, not one minuscule speck of dirt on your cap and apron is acceptable'.

The lessons continued, walking, head up shoulders back, straight, straight, straight, curtsies, deep, head down, don't stare, who do you think you are, modesty, modesty, modesty.

The day of the dinner party was rapidly approaching, Jessica's outfit was finished, the cap and apron so stiffly starched that Jessica was concerned they would crack like an egg when she put them on. Jessica carried a jug of hot water to her room, poured it into the bowl, and methodically began to wash herself with great care. Standing in the cold room one would guess that in her chemise and bloomers she would be shivering, but the excitement of the occasion had put an unusually pleasant bloom on Jessica's otherwise sallow skin. She dressed with care. Mary fussed over her, buttoning her dress and boots, tying a bow of so perfectly on Jessica's apron she hardly dare move for fear of putting it out of balance.

Jessica, along with the three other female servants and two male waiters, the footmen, the cook and a maid assembled to gather the capes and hats of the guests who were by now just beginning to arrive. They stood in the main hall, in a line so perfect that it would not put to shame the best trained guardsman.

Miss Pritchard had walked up the line inspecting the fronts

of her staff. She tied, tidied, adjusted, all that was not done to her liking, before walking back down the line inspecting their rear view. When she was satisfied everyone was presentable, she checked her watch before sending them off to their respective stations.

After the guest had been greeted, and disposed of their outdoor clothing they were shown into the drawing room where they were offered an aperitif. As soon as Jessica had taken the clothing to the small annex where they were to be stored she returned and was given the additional task of serving the drinks. The butler poured them placed the glasses with great care, carefully wiping up even the tiniest droplet spilt on the tray. Jessica then went into the drawing room attempting not to tremble so much that the glasses tinkled together.

When all the drinks had been served and any noticeable discarded glasses removed, Jessica beat a hasty retreat to the kitchen to be ready to serve the food.

After sometime, in which Jessica spent watching the elegant ladies sip their drinks and hold polite conversation. A time when she saw what she considered the most beautiful clothes in the world, the most beautiful jewels in the world, bedeck the most beautiful women in the world. The butler stepped forward with the beater to the dinner gong in his hand, gave the gong a short brush which resonated throughout the hall and thus not only provided a pause in the conversation, but a time in which the butler could make his announcement, 'Ladies and gentlemen, dinner is served'

The chatter once more intensified as the beautiful people arranged themselves, the beautiful women on the arm of their men, to be escorted into the dining hall. The dining hall shone like Aladins cave with the chandelier bedecked with candles, the candelabra on the table, made from silver, and polished so that it gleamed as if a drop of the lustrous moon had fallen to earth and alighted on the table. The mirrors on the walls had been polished so that not a trace of dust, nor the trace of a fingerprint was discernable. The table, a grand affair had been skated on by the servants wearing polishers on their shoes was liken to a rich brown soup with the fat glistening on it as the candles were reflected. The china edged in royal blue and gold, bearing the squires coat of arms, newly purchased, the crystal glasses set a ringing as the guests took theirs seat ready for the feast completed the fairy tale illusion.

The servants, in their black clothes set off by their white aprons and shirts stood silently as if they were Tutenkhamun's body guard watching over the king for his dear life. As the guests were seated the nod from the butler indicated that they, the servants were to depart in the direction of the sideboards. Placed discreetly in the anti room where the first course of gently poached, newly caught salmon decorated with a small salad was lying, already placed, in this case on the plates. With military precision the servants gathered up the plates and again when nodded to moved like a well oiled machine, forward into the dining room and presented their allotted number of guests with their fare. The room was alive with conversation, the tinkling of cutlery on plates and in sharp contrast to the atmosphere of total relaxation of the guests, the servants stood sentinel, awaiting the imperceptible command, by means of a nod to clear the plates. The sommelier and those especially trained and recruited for the evening to a higher station, move smoothly down the table, pouring wine for those thirsty enough for a fine wine to quaff quickly.

By the end of the dinner which comprised of six courses,

salmon delicate and a fine pink shade, a sorbet. This having been made from the ice preserved over the months in a newly built ice house, a real must in the high society of the day, flavoured with blackcurrants bottled by the cook at an earlier date. A rack of lamb with succulent mint sauce, new potatoes cooked with mint and rosemary, a delicate salad of young green lettuce, with optional dressing to clear the palate, before the wide variety of cheeses.

A finale of pink blancmange each one set in its own shape, which had taken cook hours of preparation wetting the moulds and measuring the exact amount. Chocolate formed in the shape of tracery leaves with a sprig of fresh redcurrants decorated the blancmange.

Once the dinner had been eaten it was time for the guests to depart into the salon, in the case of the ladies. There to partake of hot chocolate in porcelain cups imported from Japan, and small petit fours, again planned and executed over the past week by cook. She having gathered around her just like a school mistress in the classroom, all those female servants to explain the rudiments of making delicacies.

The gentlemen re-arranged their seating whilst the cigars and port were brought in with much ceremony. The wine waiter very carefully, and with much aplomb handing the decanter in an anti-clockwise route around the table, so that the gentlemen could measure their own consumption. The cigars were clipped for those who wished to smoke by James, who, then lit the 'cuban's' as trained by the butler.

By the time the table had been cleared, after the last guest had departed. The washing up had been done and the dining converted back to its pristine condition it was very late. The servants were exhausted. Jessica knew that there would be no lying in the following morning and that as automatons they were expected to be in their places as if the evening had never happened.

She wandered with the others into the kitchen, and gazed in wonder at the sight. Mrs. Lewis, against all the rules, (well it was nearly Christmas), had made enough food for a second dinner party especially for the weary bunch. They sat down, and after a few minutes in which they relaxed, were soon attacking the fare with great gusto.

After eating, Jessica was revived her excitement had been so enhanced that the only thought in her head was to hurry to her room eager to tell Mary all about the evening, she couldn't have been more excited if she had been a guest at that first dinner herself.

As she got undressed and carefully folded the clothes she had worn whilst chattering constantly about the food, the way the guests dressed, ate, spoke and drank. She chattered incessantly, and when she gazed at the opposite bed to judge Mary's reaction, Mary was sound asleep. Jessica smiled, slipped into bed, sank down under the covers, a big smile across her face, sighed and fell sound asleep, dreaming of lights, dresses, beautiful jewellery and wonderful food. A good job done by Jessica and the rest of the servants, a whole world full of variety for a young girl even if the work was long and hard.

CHAPTER 8

The following morning brought a fresh source of excitement. It was the week before Christmas, Jessica had risen as usual at five thirty, and after a wash in the ice cold water from the wash jug, she descended to the kitchen. Jessica was still serving her probationary period for the position above stairs, and therefore everyday routine tasks in the kitchen were still necessary.

Before Jessica and the others could eat breakfast, which was at 6.15am sharp there were several tasks to be performed. The below stairs servants worked a very democratic system, and as such this week it was Jessica's job to light the fire, and black lead the fireplace and stove. This must be done quickly as time was short and the kitchen really had to be fairly warm for cook's arrival. Although the stock of wood and coal to re-kindle the fire was taken in the night before, the coal scuttle must be refilled. Mrs. Lewis would chastise her well and truly if this wasn't done. Fortunately for Jessica that morning the fire was still glimmering, the ash would need to be emptied, the stove cleaned, but the job was made slightly easier.

As she entered the kitchen, however, the kitchen was icy cold despite the fire, she had sleepily lit the lamps, but the cold was unusual. She pulled her shawl around her shoulders, shivered and got to her feet after her fire duties. Jessica looked around, and noticed the rear door, leading to the passage that ultimately lead to the courtyard was ajar. Jessica looked at the door quizzically unused to this. She assumed someone had risen before her, and had gone outside leaving the door open, but then remembered it was she who had lit the lamps. She moved over to close the door, but it was only when she placed one hand on the handle to and the other flat on the door in order to push it closed, it was known for sticking in the winter, and needed a little extra effort, that she noticed splinters of fresh clean wood on the door jamb. Jessica's heart quickened, she looked around anxiously and stepped into the back hallway, she moved cautiously towards the outer door, this too was open. She realised she did not have a enough light to look around, nor did she feel safe without a light to see by . She retraced her steps lit the hurricane lamp which hung, as an extra by the low stone sink, lit it and proceeded with her investigation.

She moved toward the rear entry door that also stood open, this too had fresh wood exposed. Jessica peered outside, it was then as she, as she held the lamp high, that she noticed a glimmering light on the floor, further investigation showed two silver teaspoons in the courtyard. She stooped to pick them up, turning the spoons in her hands, she lifted the corner of her cleaning apron and wiped away the condensation which had gathered on their gleaming surface. It was as she was wiping the spoons that she suddenly realised the enormity of the situation she was in. Someone had forced an entry into the house, someone too had been into the silver pantry what else could account for the fact that the teaspoons were there?

She looked around, then, clutching the teaspoons tightly ran, as if she had wings on her feet, leaving the doors wide open as she did so, and she didn't stop until she had reached the door to Mrs. Lewis's room. Gasping for breath at first she tapped on the door, afraid of retribution at disturbing the cook, when no reply was forthcoming she knocked harder, and then as if completely taken over by the situation, hammered on the door, and shouted for Mrs. Lewis's attention.

After what appeared to be an eternity Mrs. Lewis appeared at door, she had been tending her hair when the knocking had commenced, it sounded urgent so when she answered the door one side of her rapidly greying hair had been plaited and the other was still hanging loosely around her shoulders.

'Good lord Jessica that banging is enough to wake the dead, what is it girl?' she said, hands akimbo.

'Please Mrs. Lewis, there's been a, I mean, Oh Mrs. Lewis'

Jessica said breathlessly, thrusting the silver spoon's at the Cook.

Mrs. Lewis, ever the calm efficient lady, could see the terror written all over Jessica's face. She placed her hands on Jessica's shoulders, stooped a little to look into the girl's face, held her still and gently calmed her down.

At last Jessica managed to tell Mrs. Lewis and although only a few minutes had passed, it seemed an age to Jessica.

Within the next few minutes, the alarm had been raised throughout the house, people were rushing to and fro, while Jessica rather absent minded attempted to re-light the fire, all thought of routine had long been forgotten.

The Butler and Miss Pritchard had been notified, they in

turn notified the valet who sent a rider into the town to swift-
ly summon the constabulary.

Mrs. Lewis clapped her hands together in two sharp claps,

'cum on now, the mester'll be down ere soon, an we with
a fire not yet burning well'.

The people in the kitchen, like a well oiled machine soon
set about their duties, and within fifteen minutes the kitchen
was humming at a slower but increasingly usual pace.

Miss Pritchard entered the kitchen and walked over to
where Mrs. Lewis was busy preparing the breakfast, she spoke
in a low voice that although she strained to hear Mary could
just make out the name of the master having been mentioned.

After Miss Pritchard left the kitchen, Mrs. Lewis announced
to the assembly now sitting at the kitchen table drinking
their tea that they had better drink up, make tidy the table,
as HE would be calling in five minutes. She turned and began to wet her fingers in her mouth, before smoothing them
through her now tidied hair.

Jessica was still looking pale and with the inevitable prospect of actually having to tell the Master of her findings she
was visibly shaken.

'Cum on now, pull yourself together' snapped Mrs. Lewis'

'He's not about to eat you up for breakfast, just remember to
curtsey, call him sir, an speak only after he's asked you a
question'

Jessica nodded, and made an attempt at a smile, the major
problem being, that the tears welling up in her eyes made the
effort of using those particular muscles almost impossible.

Mrs. Lewis bustled about making sure that every corner
of the kitchen was spick and span, as if there was to be a top
ranking official calling in at the army mess at any minute. In
effect as far as the kitchen staff were concerned this was just

what was about to happen to their domain.

'Get the kettle boiling, get the tray, no, the proper masters tray not that one, ' called Mrs. Lewis, as the staff ran around like scalded children.

Mrs. Lewis then once again smoothed her hair, wiped her hands on her apron, adjusted a cup and saucer with such precision it was difficult to measure, then with a loud voice crackling with anxiety yelled ' where's the tray cloth!

CHAPTER 9

A while later the butler, Jamieson, opened the door, and stood just inside the kitchen as Squire Port-Clements walked into the kitchen at a steady pace. His eyes were quick and alert as he surveyed the scene that greeted him. He surveyed everything and surveyed each and every aspect of the kitchen with its staff standing to attention with great precision.

Mrs. Lewis dropped a curtsey as the Squire spoke to her, standing with his back to the fire, hands behind his back to gather every vestige of heat possible. He slapped the palms of his hands together whilst rising to the balls of his feet, before letting them fall flat again. The Squire was a handsome man, his youthful face only showing signs of his 45 years by the thin lines at his eyes and the corners of his mouth. He had a shock of black hair, combed back with only the slightest signs of greying at his temples. He had the face of a gentle person, but with a tinge of firmness. Squire Port-Clements struggled to carry out the duty expected of a man of his standing. He rode well with the Quorn Hunt, but his seat was that of a man who really would rather not have been on a horse. He gave lavish dinner parties, but paid more attention to the table decoration and the finer details of the fare than he did his guests. In actual fact he preferred sitting in some quiet area of the estate away from prying eyes, painting, drawing or reading. He was indeed a man of more ethereal pleasures than the rombustous life expected of him.

Jessica seemed transfixed by the master, and needed to be told twice by Mrs. Lewis that the Squire would like her to step forward so he may talk to her. In the end it was Mary who stepped forward and poked her in the back that stirred Jessica out of her reverie.

She moved forward, curtsied and looked into the Squires eyes.

'So you're Jessica Jimson?' he enquired softly.

'Yes sir, I'm Jessica, I found the door open and the spoons, an' Jessica's nerves had now got the better of her. She was having great difficulty in keeping quiet, it was only on hearing Mrs. Lewis clearing her throat that she remembered the cooks words of advice and fell silent, mid sentence.

The Squire smiled understandingly, had himself had a poor experience at school and being such a mild character had long remembered his nervousness at being called to his headmaster and could see his nerves now reflected in those of Jessica. He put his hand on her shoulder as if to steady her, or to halt her escape, smiled again and said:-

'It's alright dear, if you want to tell me the whole story without stopping, I'll understand, just carry on'.

Jessica swallowed hard, rubbed her hands together and carried on with her tale, relating the whole event until:

'I ran to Mrs. Lewis's room , an she came to the door, er an er hair not even dun up'.

'Thank you Jessica" the Squire intervened at this point,

You've done very well, now I suggest you change into your best serving dress and apron, as the Constabulary will want you to tell them the tale as you've told it to me.'

'Yes sir',

said Jessica turning and was just about to make her escape at a run, when Mrs. Lewis darted forward, grabbed her by both shoulders, turned her around once more to face the Squire, whilst at the same time whispering in her ear,

'curtsey gel, thank im'

'Yes sir, thank you sir, said Jessica dropping a curtsey, 'sorry sire, may I go'.

The Squire nodded and Jessica walked as calmly as she could, the sound of her heartbeat pounding in her ears, and made her way to her room, with Mary in pursuit to fasten her buttons.

CHAPTER 10

The front part of the house was a flurry of activity, even the servants not now used to getting their hands dirty were thrown into the melee in order to dust, polish, light fires, plump cushions at a far quicker pace than they were used to. By 10am the constabulary had arrived, they had made good time from the town, and now the Inspector alighted from his carriage, his chest puffed out, shoulders back, pip in mouth and secretly excited at the prospect of beginning a piece of detection in such a grand home and for him of great importance.

The door was opened long before Inspector Thomas had reached the top step and he walked inside, after removing his hat, he was shown into the drawing room. The Squire had taken up the usual stance, warming himself by the blazing log fire. The two men shook hands before the Squire offered his visitor a seat.

'Would you care for a drink? Coffee, tea, chocolate?". Enquired the Squire.

'Not just now sir", said Inspector George Thomas, trying to

sound brusque and efficient.

'I propose we get on with the investigation before the evidence disappears".

The Squire told the Inspector the tale related by Jessica, whilst the Inspector interspersed each pause with 'Mmm' and "huhu'.

He opened and incredibly small notebook that he had taken from his breast pocket, and began to write with a small pencil, licking the tip regularly.

The Squire was at a loss to understand the reason for such a minuscule notebook.

Jessica was summoned to now attend the meeting, she entered the drawing room nervously.

'Come along Jessica, this gentleman simply wants to ask you a few questions regarding your discovery' said the Squire.

He was now sitting in the high backed wing chair alongside the blazing fire.

The Inspector cleared his throat and addressed Jessica:

'Now young missie, tell me just what you found'.

Once again Jessica related her tale. After she had finished, the Inspector moved towards her, she found his move so threatening that she stepped backwards.

'Don't worry Jessica, we are all supporting you', said the Squire.

'When you went to the back door, was it open, or did you open it?' enquired the Inspector who was in the process of attempting to re-light his pipe.

'I told you sir, it was' said Jessica.

'Wide open, or merely ajar?' the Inspector once more questioned.

'Wide open sir" answered Jessica.

'I see, thank you Jessica, if we wish to speak to you further we'll call you' said the Inspector.

'Yes sir, thank you sir', said Jessica looking over to her employer.

'You may leave us now Jessica, ask Miss Pritchard to come in as you leave', said the Squire. Jessica left and closed the large oak door gently behind her. Miss Pritchard was re-arranging the floral display on the console table she looked up as Jessica moved in her direction.

'Excuse me Miss Pritchard, could you please go to see the master'?

'Thank you Jessica, said Miss Pritchard, 'Now run along and get on with your work.'

The investigation continued, the Inspector seeing all the staff in turn. He had requested a tour of the kitchen and a careful look at the scene of the crime. The Silver Butler had completed his inventory of the silver pantry and it appeared that the pieces missing were mostly those of the very best quality. There were two other members of the constabulary in attendance and now, instead of merely guarding the near doorway where the spoons were found and the front entrance, they were called into the drawing room to see the Inspector. The Squire having made his excuses with a request to be notified of anything that was discovered.

The constable stood to attention in front of the Inspector. Their instructions were simple and straight forward, they were to attempt to find any clues which may help solve the crime.

One of their instructions which to their untrained and unimaginative minds was completely baffling, was to look very carefully at the shoes and trouser bottoms of the male staff, but to be careful not to draw attention to their investigations.

By mid-afternoon, after a meal had been served, the house

had settled down, to at least something resembling normality, the constables returned to the drawing room to report their findings to the Inspector.

'Stand each side of the door please', said the Inspector, 'and only move when instructed to do so'.

The inspector bent down to the large log basket, and fished amongst the logs, picking up several small splinters of wood. These he placed carefully in his hand. He walked towards the door, opened it, picked up the small bell on the console table and rang it. It wasn't many seconds before the butler appeared.

'Yes sir,' he said curtly.

'I would like to see yourself, the groom the footman and the masters valet please', said the Inspector.

'All together sir?' said the butler, eyebrows raising questionably.

The gentlemen of the staff assembled in the drawing room, all standing regimented in a line before the Inspector.

'Gentlemen" announced the Inspector, 'I feel our investigations are nearing their conclusions. I've asked you gentlemen to assist me in bringing my Investigations to a satisfactory end.'

They looked from one to the other.

'who do you think did it sir'? asked Jamieson the Butler

'Well, before I tell you that, let me explain what I have been looking for. I've been searching for the splinters broken off the back door when entry was forced, you see, we haven't found them I suspect the burglar picked them up and of course possibly threw them into the fire'.

The Inspector moved towards the gentlemen and walked in front of them looking into their eyes as he passed them, midway he opened his fingers and let the wood splinters drop to the floor.

'However, he could of course have not noticed that these fragments from the door had lodged in his clothing and may still be there. Hello, what's this, he glanced at the floor, and bent slowly to the floor to pick up the splinters'.

The groom suddenly made a bolt for the door. With a nod of the head from the Inspector, the two constables moved forward to block his exit.

The footman yelled. 'You stupid sod, e didn't know, e didn't know, I swept everything up, there was nothing to find'

The two were formally charged, handcuffed and taken to the waiting cart to be driven to the town gaol.

Squire Port-Clements spoke to the Inspector at length before giving his congratulations,

'well done, well done, how did you know?'

'I didn't sir, it was a long shot, I had no clue, no evidence, in fact the crime was well executed with the exception of the fact that the spoons were dropped and no self respecting criminal would have been that careless', the Inspector explained with signs of great self satisfaction written all over his face.

The silver was discovered inside the hay above the stables, and after it had been carefully cleaned, it was placed back in the silver pantry where it belonged, this time, much to the embarrassment of the butler, the key was also subsidised by a padlock to ensure no further problems. The keys were to be held only by the silver butler and the Squire to further protect the property.

Jessica enjoyed her hour of fame, but by the next morning, everything was again running smoothly and the incident was on the way to becoming an interesting piece of history to keep any newcomers to the staff amused.

CHAPTER 11

Christmas arrived, a tree was cut from the estate and taken into the drawing room. The family were gathered together, and had placed a quantity of decorations on it. The rest of the decorations were placed behind the tree in their box from where they would miraculously be placed on the large green edifice before the family convened the following day.

The cook was busy directing her staff, Mary was working overtime on the mincing machine, reducing the onions to near pulp, with an almost musical sound coming from her corner of the kitchen. The crunching of fresh onion, the turning of the handle interspersed by a sniff, and a snuffle as the tears streamed down Mary's face.

Jessica was sitting on a stool at the large kitchen table, hands red and sore as she continually dipped her hands in the large bowl of ice cold water to take the peel from yet another potato.

As an essential part of the Christmas preparations the making of the Christmas pudding was a ceremony that dated back many years. Every member of the household, family and servants alike were to stir the pudding, making a wish for their future.

Jessica's special wish was for a certain young man to have been invited to the family dinner where Jessica would be serving. Jessica had seen the young man enter the house on several occasions, each time she felt her heart pounding so loudly that she felt sure it could be heard throughout the house. Her face became hot and flushed culminating in Jessica spending the next few moments looking at the floor and shuffling her feet. She could describe in detail the smallest pattern on the tiles that covered the floor in the hall. Jessica was of course well aware of the futility of her admiration for such a person, her feelings were so strong that each night before she went to bed, she would close her eyes so tightly and attempt to conjure up every detail of his face.

The young man, for his part, felt equally drawn to Jessica, and was equally well aware of the fact that such a liaison was impossible.

Jemes Conserton was indeed a guest at the Christmas dinner that year he was accompanied by his parents and his sister Victoria.

When dinner was announced, the party glided into the dining room, the table looked a picture, with its glistening glassware, gleaming silver and a twisted garland of holly, ivy mistletoe, along with a number of Christmas roses. The garland took up the full length of the dining table.

Standing like statues in their stiffly starched aprons and caps, the servants, each holding silver trays loaded with an array of seafood which was served as soon as the family and guests were seated. Before serving the assembled group of servants awaited a nod from the butler, it was only then that the well oiled machine was set in motion.

The dinner progressed with vegetables accompanied by meats of Goose, and pork not before the head of the pig, suitably decorated and piped completed with an apple in the mouth. This bought forth applause from the assembly.

The goose was placed before the master, who ceremoniously carved the first slice. The meat platter was then removed and set upon the highly polished buffet in order for the butler to continue the carving.

The initial noise of a group of people sitting down for dinner subsided, as soon as plates with food were placed before the assembled group the sound changed completely. The music now was only that of the scraping of knives and forks and the satisfying chink of glasses. Occasionally, as the party moved through their fare could be heard a gentle mumble of part conversation or low laughter.

Jessica stood against the dining room wall, salivating, as were the rest of the waiting on staff, each longing to leave the room, but at the same time wanting to stay in order to simply gaze at the beautiful dresses and equally beautiful wearers.

Jessica wanted to stay simply in order to gaze at James Conserton. Several times during the meal he turned his head towards her and although not smiling with his mouth, let his eyes do the talking. James knew that his mother Lady Conserton was sitting opposite, he above all others was well aware that she would not hesitate to ensure Jessica was no longer employed if he had shown any interest at all, especially if she had reciprocated.

The pudding was wheeled into the dining room on a trolley. The brandy poured over the pudding, lit while the assembly sang. Two hours after the start of the meal was over and the guests left the dining room, some to take the air, some to retire to their rooms for a rest, whilst others went into the drawing room to play games of a gentle and non active nature.

By three pm the servants were sitting down at a beautifully decorated servants table and tucking into a meal equal to that of their employer, complete with a glass of wine. Jessica only taking two sips before she felt, first her neck and then her cheeks begin to burn. Mrs. Lewis looked up and laughed as she passed an enormous jug containing water.

'no more of that stuff for you gel, ere drink a tumbler of water'

This of course drew most of the others eyes to Jessica and the laughter at her expense echoed around the room.

At seven in the evening Jessica was given permission to visit her family. Mrs. Lewis having carefully parcelled enough food to ensure for the next few days at least the family would not go hungry.

Jessica put on her hat and coat and left to make the chilly journey to her home. She had been told to ensure she was back in order to be on duty by six o'clock the following morning. She carefully closed the door behind her, and stepped into the stable yard, the air was crisp, the night sky clear, and the stars twinkling like tiny fragments of broken crystal glass.

Jessica walked along the drive, and was just passing the church when she felt she was not alone.

'May I escort you"? a voice she did not recognise seemed to be coming from the wall

She stopped, afraid, she had heard stories of men being somewhat unkind to young girls, should she run? Should she scream?

'Who are you'? she asked voice trembling with fear.

Out into the driveway stepped James. He was taller than

she had previously thought, and as far as she could make out just as handsome as she already knew.

'I'm going home, I know the way Sir' she said in a soft whisper.

'I only wish to walk alongside you, I promise I've no intention of taking advantage of my situation' he said gently.

'Very well Sir' she said, she began to walk increasing the speed of her advance.

They walked along, neither speaking, both walking with eyes looking immediately ahead, but not seeing anything. At last they reached the gate, Jessica did not want the driveway to end, neither did James. However, the end had indeed come, Jessica stopped.

'Thank you sir, I appreciated your company' she said shyly

'And I yours um'

'Jessica sir'

'Jessica, I'll not forget that name', he said gently, leaning forward touching her arm.

Jessica pulled away sharply, afraid not only of him, but also afraid of herself.

'Goodbye sir', she said brusquely.

'Take care' she whispered, as he quickly disappeared into the darkness of the cold Christmas evening.

James walked back to the hall, head down as he realised at last how futile his hopes really were. Jessica too realised the hopelessness of the situation. She quickened her step and by the time she had completed the remaining walk to her home was quite out of breath.

Jessica's mother was busy standing at the rough scrubbed table kneading bread. The inviting smell of warm yeast pervaded the room and mingled with the smell of leek and potato soup that was bubbling away over the fire.

'Hello mam' said Jessica, face ruddy with the cold evening air, and the excitement of the previous encounter.

'Hello gel, I'm glad you've come, I cud to with a spare pair of ands, can you get the salt from the cupboard', she said wearily.

CHAPTER 12

Jessica visited her mother regularly, each time she saw her the more forgetful and older she looked. Her mother used always to be on the move, always seemed full of energy. Since Jessica's father had died her mother seemed to have lost the will to live.

On this visit as soon as her bread making was complete. Jessica's mother sat down in the large Windsor chair that her father always sat in. She rubbed her hands on her apron, blew a wisp of hair in the air that had fallen out of place and gave a nervous laugh.

'Well gel, I'm worn out, an me not needing to do half as much as I used to'.

Jessica smiled and moved over to the large chair, her mother rested her hand on Jessica's shoulder and Jessica gently stroked her head and kissed her mothers white streaked hair.

'I love you Mam, I really do. I just wish I could stay home and look after you, but I'll come as often as I can, an bring you good food'

Jessica bit her lower lip, she'd heard her mother say how tired her grandmother had become by the age of fifty, and here was her mother, a reflection of the story she had told Jessica. That night was to be one of the last she was to spend at her family home.

The following morning on her way back to the hall she entered the church and threw herself on the floor crying uncontrollably;-

'please, please God, don't take her, she's all I really have left, please don't do that. I love you, but oh how I love Mam, please, please'

Jessica was twenty when her mother died, although she had been continually unwell for years, her final illness had been short lived. Jessica was with her when she died, she was sitting beside her mothers' bed she was holding the fragile hand, inspecting the fingers which had produced beautiful needlework in their time. Her mother had also produced the stiff, beautifully woven baskets in their time, It was when those worn fingers curled over Jessica's own small hand and those dark rimmed eyes looked at Jessica she said,

'Take care gel, tell the others I love them, you'll always be their mother now, I love you gel'

It was with those words she closed her eyes, breathed what Jessica though was a deep sigh, but as the fingers relaxed their grip Jessica realised her mother was no longer in that frail body. She loosened her mother's hand, stroked the relaxed brow, kissed her mother's cooling cheeks and went out of the room to where her brothers and sisters were waiting.

The funeral took place in the rain, their feet grew heavy with the mud, and the prayers were cut short. Jessica placed a spray of chrysanthemums on the coffin on that wet October day and as the coffin was lowered gently into the cold wet earth, the little gathering turn quietly and walked away a page of their history now turned.

CHAPTER 13

That Christmas Jessica was given the position of under housekeeper, a prestigious job, working and learning a new art directly from Miss Pritchard. Miss Pritchard was a hard task master, insisting on a knowledge of accounts, in addition to above stairs knowledge that Jessica was quick to pick up. The accounts were another thing, now Jessica had to delve into the recesses of her mind, using pounds she had never thought were necessary, her grounding had, however, proved invaluable.

That year, for Jessica it was difficult to attend church, although in her heart she knew that her faith upheld her, she felt that she really had needed her mother more than God. Why did she have to be taken away? The answer never came, she simply ultimately accepted that this was indeed the way of the world and nothing she could ever have done would change this.

The way forward was eventually found. Mrs. Lewis had noticed Jessica's sadness, and realised the general cause. She suggested that the next time she was to attend chapel that Jessica join her. Mrs. Lewis was quietly filling the role of Jessica's mother a role both were happy with.

Jessica found a new and refreshing insight into her beliefs, she silently promised to try her utmost to help and support others and not to dwell of her own problems, which with hindsight seemed insignificant compared with others. Still she did pray for her one dream or prayer to be answered, which was that young James Conserton would once again come to the hall to visit. That they could once again walk side by side and that she be pleasant and discuss things in a mature way. This at least she knew, that it was only a dream, a dream with an impossible satisfactory conclusion, but it was hers, and no one could ever interfere with her dream or take it away.

CHAPTER 14

Jessica was kept busy. She had thrown herself into her work, she had, in fact, become an excellent first assistant to Miss Pritchard. Jessica was working one day alongside Miss Pritchard when Geraldine, the daughter of the master, who was about the same age as Jessica appeared at the doorway.

'I'm sorry to disturb you at your work, but it's so quiet here today, I can't settle to read and it's too wet to go for a walk, so I decided to go for a walk around the house.'

'That's alright miss, you're very welcome, can I get you anything.?'

Well no, but I've seen you around, I can see that you're about the same size as me and I thought this may be of use to you.'

Geraldine held out her arms in which were cradled a lovely day dress. The dress was made from fine cotton with tiny rosebuds embroidered around the skirt.

'It's been mended, but the mend was very well done'

'Jessica did not know what to say, she well knew that she

must never receive anything from others in the house unless another person was there to verify the gift. She also knew well where the mend was, as she was the one who had done it.

'Thank you miss, but I'm sorry I can't.

'Oh how stupid, of course you must have a witness to the gift, I'll find Miss Pritchard'.

Miss Pritchard was found and the gift made. Jessica was thrilled with the gift, she also knew that the only time she would be able to wear it was on going to church, as where else can a mere servant wear something as elegant as this. She could well be accused of being too pretentious.

Geraldine had left, both girls with the feeling that although there were class differences too great to bridge, they liked each other and in another age could have become friends.

There was great excitement as the day was the first of May. As usual the master would host a May Ball. The day was hot, the work hard, everything as had happened at Christmas the house was decorated this time with flowers and ribbons. The local school had decorated the May pole and after hours of practise the children could now weave a bower as accurately as a lace worker using her skill with bobbins to weave a beautiful lace.

There was much chattering and excitement, Mrs. Lewis was directing operations regarding the feast. Miss Pritchard and Jessica were busy checking and double checking that gifts were wrapped and the dining room perfect in every way.

Louise, who was Geraldine's maid had fallen ill, it was thought with a bilious attack, but extra care was taken with the boiling of water and the washing of crockery and cutlery. Typhoid was still a problem when many people were living under the same roof. Just look at poor Queen Victoria widowed so young. A few weeks later it was discovered she was pregnant, and discretely married one of the junior cattle hands.

Geraldine had a very special reason in wanting to look especially attractive that evening. The honourable Paul Reeming the son of Lord and Lady Reeming would be attending the May Ball. Geraldine, it was known, had taken walks around the garden with this young man when he visited on more than one occasion. It was thought that she might have an arrangement.

Geraldine was extremely concerned over the absence of her maid, after all who would dress her hair? It wasn't the most beautiful feature of this pretty girl, therefore extra attention was needed to make the best possible job.

Miss Pritchard was summoned to Miss Geraldine's room, Once there Geraldine spoke to Miss Pritchard, who nodded, smiled and then sent a maid to summon Jessica.

'Jessica, Miss Porth-Clements has a problem, Louise is indisposed and therefore unable to tend Miss Geraldine in her toilet for this evening. You are of a similar age, and you do have a very artistic flair, as I have seen from your embroidery. Miss Geraldine and I are of the opinion that you can help Miss Geraldine in her preparations.'

Miss Pritchard placed her hand on Jessica's shoulder and gave it a little squeeze of reassurance.

'But what about my tasks downstairs Miss Pritchard' said Jessica anxiously.

'Don't worry we've almost finished anyway dear, you just go up with Miss Geraldine', Miss Pritchard was checking her list, 'we'll manage'.

As they entered Miss Geraldine's room, Geraldine sat on the bed buried her head in her hands and wept bitterly.

'What's the problem Miss?' said Jessica moving towards

her mistress longing to comfort her, but knowing that was not her place.

'How can I look pretty Jessica, I want so much to be my best this evening', Geraldine said choking on her tears.

'Don't worry miss, we'll make out, don't worry, now I'll just nip to the kitchen for a few things whilst you ring Mary for the bath water, sorry miss, I didn't wish to order you about', said Jessica dropping a curtsey as she left the room.

Once in the kitchen Jessica asked Mrs. Lewis for malt vinegar and cochineal, once equipped with these she quickly returned to Miss Geraldine's room. She entered just as Mary was leaving with an empty bucket.

'Core you ain't arf gorra job on Jess', she said looking at Jessica pitifully.

'No trouble I know exactly what I'm doing', said Jessica with confidence, and indeed she did have quite set ideas on just how she would dress Miss Geraldine's hair.

Jessica set about washing Geraldine's hair before she entered her bath. Geraldine had some misgivings when Jessica produced the vinegar to rinse into Geraldine's hair. She was however, so concerned to look her best she agreed she would try anything once.

After her bath, Jessica began the job of drying Miss Geraldine's thick hair. Geraldine sat passively at the dressing table. Geraldine's thick and straight hair was in good condition, the colour was a mousy shade with a hint of chestnut. As Jessica gently brushed Geraldine put a hand up to prevent the next brush stroke.

'Jessica' she exclaimed, 'Jessica what have you done?'

'Sorry Miss I don't understand', said Jessica with a hint of alarm in her voice.

'It shines, Jessica, I've never seen my hair shine so before, how did you do it?' Geraldine exclaimed with excitement in her voice.

'Vinegar miss, always guaranteed to make hair shine', Jessica resumed her brushing.

When the hair was dry, Geraldine, who had been discussing her dress moved to the wardrobe and took out a delicate pink silk dress decorated with tiny rosebuds. The sleeves were voluminous, and across the bodice was a large gathering of rosebuds. Geraldine shook the dress, and laid it across the bed.

'Oh miss it's beautiful, so beautiful,' said Jessica clenching her hands together.

'You really like it Jessica, can you make me beautiful enough to fit the dress?' enquired Geraldine.

'Miss, you are beautiful, all I can do is decorate a little"

Jessica put a little cochineal on Geraldine's lips, assuring her that by the time she was ready the crimson would have been moistened enough and faded just enough so as to have added an interesting hint of colour to her lips.

Geraldine's hair was indeed beautifully dressed with a complicated pattern of thick and thin plaits interwoven, a few of the roses that decorated the bodice of the dress were removed and placed in her hair. The dress buttoned, the cream silk hose checked for wrinkles, the pretty shoes placed on her feet and Geraldine was ready.

The over all result had the desired effect, young Paul was swept off his feet, although Jessica suspected the decoration was not needed. A few weeks later Paul Reeming made an appointment to see Geraldine's father.

The day after May day Geraldine sent a purple cotton dress to Jessica with her thanks for her services.

CHAPTER 15

Jessica was given a day off with thanks by Geraldine.

It was a warm fine day, she put on her new dress, and a bonnet and after some deliberation decided she would go for a walk to a place she had been used to frequenting when she was a small girl.

She walked down the drive, across the road and towards the town, until she reached the river. The old mill stood on the junction of two roads. Jessica entered the field leading to a place where the river was, as a rule shallow enough to swim, a spot that was frequented by young men on a Sunday afternoon. The men would walk down the lane which divided some fields, a short walk of some mile or so, in to summer a very popular meeting point. It was not today, however, Sunday, the place was peaceful and much to Jessica's liking.

Jessica felt a sudden urge to run as fast and as hard as she could. She lifted her skirts above her black laced boots and hat in hand, skirts flying she dashed across the field, falling laughing on the grassy bank know locally as the Daisy Bank.

The area had once held a manor or a monastery of some

description before Cromwell's army had destroyed it.

When she had regained her breath she stopped and looked around. She tidies her dress around her before leaning back, hands behind her head and gazing at a small white cloud, which she convinced herself looked like old father times beard must look like. Once again a smile spread over her face.

Jessica lay in this position soaking up the luxury of time to dream before getting to her feet. Hat in hand she walked on, stooping to pick the delicate pink lady smock and tucking each successive stem into the ribbon of her hat.

Jessica eventually reached the newly erected bridge over the river and sat at the water's edge. After several anxious looks to ensure no one was around she quickly removed her boots and then her stockings, putting the latter into the pocket of her dress. She lay the flower bedecked hat next to her boots and let her toes touch the surface of the water. After the initial shock of the cold liquid she quickly immersed her feet up to her ankles in the river.

Jessica gazed at the slow flowing water and said softly,

' do you know water, now I know what is meant by the saying 'a lot of water has passed under the bridge. I used to think it so silly, but oh how my life has changed since I last came to sit by your edge'.

Jessica fell silent, and let the first of her tears trickle down her cheeks, flipping drops from the end of her nose with the back of her hand.

Jessica was suddenly aware of the sound of horse's hooves on the narrow lane that was the nearest piece of footpath and road to this part of the river. After a while she heard a strong male voice call 'whoa',

Jessica looked up and saw a handsome young man at the

reins of a cart, in the cart was a family group consisting of man, woman and three children. The whole family alighted. The children initially appeared to run in every direction shouting and running with a new found freedom, unaware that they were being seen and overheard. The man alighted next and assisted the woman, they strolled towards the river arm in arm, whilst the driver of the cart loosed the reins to enable the horse to crop the grass in the lane, he then leaned back in the seat, cap pulled forward to shade his eyes from the sun to enjoy the relative peace and quiet whilst the family were away.

Jessica decided she was still enjoying her solitude and rose as the family approached. She quickly dried her feet on the grass, replacing her boots, her stockings would have to wait, then, hat firmly on her head she set off back the way she had come.

When she reached the first part of the ruined wall she was startled by a stone, that appeared to have come from nowhere, but landed at her feet. She stopped and looked around, but could see nothing, when suddenly, the young man, who had been driving the cart leapt over the wall and landed at her feet.

Jessica tried to move to the side, but he too moved, this balancing dance lasted a few moments until, Jessica hands on hips, temper rising said:

'don't be a fool, just you let me pass'

' a kiss first' said the cheeky young man.

'Never, you're disgusting', said Jessica, 'now let me pass', again she moved to the side, this time he grabbed her by both arms and attempted to kiss her. Jessica was terrified, but at the same time was now extremely angry. She kicked out, her small boots finding their mark on his shinbone, he immediately released her and reeled back in pain.

Jessica did not run, she felt very confident now, she simply strode away, her right hand holding the crown of her hat, her left holding her skirt to ease the movement. After a few yards, she turned and shouted over her shoulder.

'you disgusting object, don't you think it's time you re-membered the manners your mother taught you, or didn't she teach you anything at all?'

The young man realised that this young woman was not one of the flighty girls he was used to encountering and in a voice too low to be heard said:

'I'll see you again missy, in fact, I'll see more of you than you care to think about'.

He then turned and sidled back to his cart, heart pounding to resume his wait for the passengers.

CHAPTER 16

Jessica walked quickly across the field and after some time her anger subsided, she slowed down to a more gentle pace, her day off had been shattered, her relaxed mood was now at an end.

She strolled back towards the hall. Halfway up the road she heard horse hooves clopping on the road, it was only as the horse drew near that she breathed a sigh of relief. Initially she had been concerned that the young man had followed her, now she could see that this horse was coming from the direction of the hall and was in fact Tom Jennings the new stable hand on his way to the town to collect the orders for the hall.

Tom saw Jessica walking along the road and could see by her rosy cheeks that all had not gone well with her day. He pulled up the cart and leant towards her.

'Want a ride to town Jess? You've still got a good while left, too long to want to go back to the hall yet awhile'.

Jessica looked into his pleasant face, with blue eyes, which seemed to sparkle with the joy of living.

'Yes please Tom, that's a lovely idea', she said smiling.

She held out her hand to be assisted into the cart. Once settled on the seat they set off at a steady pace. As they went on their way they chatted. Jessica explained about her family and told Tom that her two sisters lived in the town. In fact, she thought she might call in the hopes of being able to see them. Tom dropped Jessica off in the town centre and promised to meet her at the same spot four hours later.

Jessica set off to visit Emma. Emma lived and worked in a large house on the main Leicester road of the town. It took Jessica only five minutes to reach the house. She walked around to the servant's entrance and knocked at the door. A young girl who reminded Jessica of herself all those years ago when she had begun in service opened the door. Jessica was allowed into the kitchen and sat at the well-scrubbed table.

It was always unusual for servants to have casual callers, but on this occasion Emma was permitted to entertain her sister.

They sat at the well-scrubbed kitchen table to drink tea and eat delicious scones. Whilst they ate Emma told Jessica that she had met a very good man who had asked her to marry him.

Emma was not particularly beautiful and at the ripe age of twenty-six was beginning to loose her youthful bloom.

The man she was about to marry was a farmer from a near-by village, he was reasonably well provided for and actually owned a large farm house complete with a cook and some-one came twice each week to clean for him. Jessica thought Emma had really done well for herself and wished her sister well for the future.

The farmer lived alone and therefore at the age of twenty-eight thought it expedient for him to find a good wife and perhaps provide children who not only could care for them both in old age, but also take over the farm in the future. John Lorimer, had met Emma when he had called at her employers house to discuss investment, as Emma's employer was a local banker.

Emma told Jessica that she wished all her family to attend the wedding, the boys actually worked for a neighbouring farmer in the same village where she was to make her home, as the farmers would be neighbours she thought there may be little problem in them being allowed time off to attend their sisters wedding. Emma saw Clara regularly, so that left Jessica who now knew about the forthcoming event.

Jessica was sorry now that she hadn't taken any money with her, what little savings she had could have been put to good use in purchasing a new shawl for the wedding. She hugged Emma and left to pay now a much shorter visit to Clara.

Clara was pleased to see her sister and excited about the forthcoming wedding. She herself had met a man who wished to consider marriage, but for the time being she had declined his offer as he was a widower with two children. He too was reasonably well off and she, at the age of twenty eight knew that the prospects of meeting a bachelor were slim, but all the same she knew this gentleman would wait.

Eventually Jessica made her way to the spot where she was to meet Tom, as she turned the corner she saw he was waiting for her. She acknowledged him and clambered up beside him they set off home, the sun still shining down on the now later day and Jessica was feeling hungry.

They arrived at the hall and as Jessica entered the door to the kitchen she could smell the sweetness of newly made rice pudding, she couldn't help thinking back to when her family was truly a family and visualising the children rushing in after hours playing in the surrounding fields tired but hungry. Jessica shook herself into reality and greeted her companions cheerfully.

CHAPTER 17

After Jessica had been such a success with Miss Geraldine, she was given the opportunity to become her maid, she declined the offer explaining her interests lay far more in the area of household matters rather than anything else.

Jessica continued with her work with Miss Pritchard, but also still assisting in the kitchen when she was needed. Mrs. Lewis has taught many things including the crafts of knitting and crochet. She wished to repay her by helping when she could. Mrs. Lewis had of late been unwell and occasionally Jessica had stepped in to assist with the preparation of meals in order that the master and mistress did not hear of Mrs. Lewis's incapacity. They all knew that a sick servant was no longer a viable investment and therefore it was usual to request their relinquishing their posts.

In late summer, Mrs. Lewis sat down in her chair to have her statutory afternoon nap, when Mary attempted to wake her, she was no longer in this world, but had drifted into a sleep never to awaken. This of course threw the whole house into turmoil and dinner that evening was certainly a fete' acomplis, with everyone in the kitchen assisting in its preparation in between tears and nose blowing. Mary proved a tower of strength, she had always paid close attention to Mrs. Lewis and as a result was requested to take charge in a temporary capacity whilst Miss Pritchard put advertisements in the newspapers and prepared to interview applicants for the post. However, Mary proved, to all, that she was capable of holding the post, even though a little inexperienced in the finer detail. She was trusted to work in the post and at the age of twenty-seven years had achieved something of a coup.

CHAPTER 18

The day of Emma's wedding had arrived. Jessica had managed to get once again the whole day off. That morning Jessica awoke to the birds chattering and the sun shining. My sister is going to have the best day ever, announced Jessica to herself largely although of course she was overheard by Mary who still shared her room. Soon the two were chattering animatedly about the forthcoming event. After the daily chores were finished and Mary had completed her duties of preparing breakfast for the household the two girls went upstairs. Mary dressed Jessica's hair and buttoned her into the purple dress which Miss Geraldine had donated, her hat was bedecked with a new ribbon in pale pink which hung in two streamers down her back, she had no need for a shawl after all, the day was fine and warm. The mistress had given permission to pick some late summer roses, which had been made into an attractive posy to be carried at the wedding, the roses consisted in the main of a pale pink variety, which complemented the purple dress perfectly.

Jessica managed to get a lift to the village, and walked the short distance to the church, there she found Clara waiting for her with the boys. Thomas, being the elder of the boys was to give his sister away and Jim was acting as usher. Jessica could not help thinking how tall and handsome her brothers had become, both bearing a striking resemblance to their father, with the exception of the eyes, which were the image of their mother.

Emma turned up in a small cart decorated with swages of seasonal flowers, and the seat covered with red velvet. Emma's dress was of beige cotton, embroidered in pink and burgundy, her hair plaited and coiled with pink roses in the centre of the coil, she carried a bouquet of michaelmas daises that perfectly toned Jessica's dress.

The groom, in the form of George Bassford, a fine name, was waiting in the church as the tiny procession of Emma on Thomas's arm followed by Clara and Jessica walked slowly down the aisle. Emma smiled shyly as she stood before the minister. It was obvious Jessica thought, that George Bassford did really care for Emma and not, in a previous time of sadness, merely want a capable housewife.

The marriage proceeded without a hitch and the reception held at the newly married couples' local hostelry, 'The Hammer and Pincers'. The fare was adequate, and the beer newly tapped and of good condition. Jessica, however, did not imbibe due to her new found religion.

At the end of the merrymaking the little family kissed each other, kissed the happy couple and wished them every happiness then made their way to their respective homes.

To Jessica, it seemed no time at all until first Clara succumbed to the endearments of her beau, followed by Thomas and Jim, leaving only herself, now at the ripe old age of thirty years of age, now far too old to be snapped up.

CHAPTER 19

That Christmas followed the usual pattern, parties, dinners and entertaining on a grand scale.

One evening Jessica was once again waiting at table when amongst the guests she spotted James Conserton. She had not seen this gentleman for some five years, she had learned from careful listening, that, he had been on 'the Grand Tour' after which he had joined the diplomatic service and had been stationed in India. India was a country Jessica knew little about with the exception of the fact that the women wore beautiful clothes and themselves were as beautiful as their clothes.

James nodded to Jessica as he entered the room and during the evening, as she was serving the food made sure that his hand was placed in such a way that it was unavoidable for her not to brush against it as she served dinner. Jessica felt the thrill of this contact reverberate throughout the whole of her body. She quickly told herself she was not in the slightest interested in his dreamed of advances. In reality all she wanted to do was to rush into his arms and him to hold her tightly and tell her he loved her. Stupid woman she rebuked herself, look at you thirty years old and definitely no lady.

She was angry with herself for allowing this moment of weakness, but she could not help her feelings. Over the next few days her feelings became stronger, culminating in something that Jessica would remember and cherish for the rest of her life.

It happened one evening after dinner. Jessica had gone into the grounds surrounding the hall in order to attempt to get her troubled mind back into some semblance of order. She was leaning against a wall, gazing at the stars, heart pounding, thoughts a confusing jumble, when her solitude was disturbed by a voice coming from the direction of a near-by oak tree.

'I'm sorry, Jessica, I do wish I could help us by not paying you attention, but even though I know our plight is an impossible dream I still cannot avoid the attention I pay you'.

It was James Conserton, he had gone into the garden and over the beech hedge had spotted Jessica.

'Sir', said Jessica

'I wish to know nothing of your desires, I am I know not of your class, but I am no ones fool. I've seen and heard of too many poor girls being discarded by Gentlemen like yourselves, and to spend a great deal of time in the workhouse as a result of advances made to them.'

'My desires', interjected James, ' may be of mortal kind, but my love will last far longer. I'm afraid you have captivated me, I wish for no one else in my life. I cannot take you for a wife and I will not ask you to be my wife and not to be able to use my name, that is wrong and always will be so'.

He was, as Jessica could see quite sincere, which was to prove so for all time, as James Conserton would indeed never marry and never stop loving the woman who was totally unobtainable.

79

CHAPTER 20

Jessica moved even further into her religion, she seemed more solitary than ever and became deeper involved in her work. She had by now progressed in her work to such a degree that not only did she work as assistant to Miss Pritchard, but also became the very private confidant to Miss Geraldine as she still affectionately knew her.

She was now entitled, because of her seniority, to one full day off each week. It was on one of these days off when she was walking in the cool autumn rain, that she once again met the young man who had been so rude to her at Daisy Bank . She was standing by a gate, gazing out across the open countryside, thinking of nothing in particular, when she heard a voice.

'Ere we are again, can I av a kiss this time then?', he was standing pitchfork in hand laughing coarsely.

'You seem duty bound to ruin my days off', she said crossly, 'just clear off an leave me alone'.

'You're on my patch today love, I'm working in the barn just there', he pointed to a ramshackle barn just yards from where Jessica had been standing and she hadn't even noticed it.

'I'll move then, said Jessica, turning and walking away.

'Just a minute, if you won't give me a kiss, will you just be civil and give me a smile', his laughing ruddy face, with huge overgrown moustache, which left his features out of balance had suddenly become soft, although his eyes still looked full of devilment.

'I thought you were supposed to be working, an I've no desire to get anyone in trouble, beside it's just coming on to rain and I'm just about to return home' Jessica said softening her tone.

'I suppose I am, well just tell me your name an I'll be satisfied, for today anyway', he said more gently.

'The name's Jessica, an as I said before, who said I'd be seeing you again'.

'I'll mek sure we do somehow Jess, cos I've taken a liking to you, as I never av to a woman before'. With that he touched his cap and strolled away in the direction of the barn, pitchfork over his shoulder and whistling 'All things bright and beautiful'.

Jessica quickened her step and pulled her shawl well over her head, as the rain was coming down hard now and a wind had got up, blowing the last of the remaining Autumn leaves from the trees.

By the time she reached the hall she was soaked, fortunately she was now in her own room and having Mary as a very good friend had its advantages. On reaching her room she had found a blazing fire in the grate and the old hip bath used by her employers before they had a new bath with hot and cold running water, which was powered by a huge geyser, was standing near the open fire. Alice, the young under maid was detailed to begin to fill the bath with hot water as soon as Jessica was heard in the house and a goodly helping of mustard was added to ward off any cold.

Once bathed and dried, with clean dry clothes put on Jessica sat on her bed, brush in hand brushing her hair. As she brushed with long slow strokes, she ruminated on the day's events. She was certain more than anything in the world that her love and deep affection would always belong to James Conserton, but at the same time could not help feeling somewhat drawn to the rough young man with the overgrown moustache. She suddenly remembered she didn't even know who he was. Oh well, she thought, if I'm meant to get to know him better, then no doubt I will, nothing gained nothing lost.

CHAPTER 21

The first Thursday nearest to November 11th 'All Saints Day' drew near. This was the date of the fair beginning in the town that lasted until Saturday evening 10 O'clock sharp. An event, which had changed dramatically over the intervening years since Jessica had first set eyes on it. It was now full of coloured lights, music and fun rides, all powered by giant steam engines which puffed out clouds of black sulphur ridden smoke, which, due to the fact that in November the air was already moist, the smell of the smoke hung low over the who market place where the fair was centred. The smell permeated clothes, hair and even bodies, but no one seemed to mind this inconvenience as the excitement was well worth the temporary discomfort.

It was this year that Geraldine had at last proposed to by Paul Reeming. He had been in chambers for a number of years and was now, he considered successful enough to take Geraldine as his wife and to be able to provide for her as he wished. The waiting had been hard and it was fairly unheard of for a woman to wait so long, after all she was considered to be on the threshold of middle age.

The relief of Squire Port-Clements to the news of this event was so great, that he arranged for no less than three carts to be made available in order that any of the staff who so wished, could enjoy a few hours at the fair over the three evenings it was there.

The Friday evening had been chosen by Jessica because, having written to her sister Emma, she had arranged to meet her under the newly erected Town Hall clock at seven in the evening.

Friday arrived, the night had once again had a touch of frost in the air, but at the same time it had been fairly warm during the day. As they passed over the river, the first signs of a mist that could so easily turn into a fog was drifting idly over the fields and roadway. Although as yet too insignificant to be picked up in the small lamps carried by some of the carts' occupants.

Jessica arrived at the Town Hall by six fifty five, Emma was already waiting, stamping her feet and throwing her arms about her body. She wore a short brown cape with a high collar of fur over her black serge dress and had a shawl over her head, neatly tucked into the cape.

'Hello Jess, it's lovely to see you again, how are you?"

'Fine, I'm fine and yourself?' enquired Jessica.

'Well, I'm fine considering".

'considering what?' enquired Jessica allowing a hint of concern in her voice.

'Well Jess, your to be an aunty, just imagine, a whole new generation starting up, I wonder how they'll all fare?' Emma said with a wistful note in her voice.

'They, they'? said Jessica, 'who says they'll be more?'

'Well there's five of us and four already married, I bet you'll join us soon, can't see you left on the shelf forever, you're too good and kind for that and anyhow it's been years now since we were all married. I thought there must be something wrong with all of us, but now I've started the trend maybe others will follow soon'.

'Enough of that talk,' interjected Jessica, 'we'll get no fair in before you have to meet your husband at this rate, let's get on with the visit, specially if it's to be me last wi mi sister before she gets erself really tied to the house'. Jessica said, trying to imagine herself as an aunt and her sister as a mother.

They strolled through the fair, they sampled the candy-floss, toffee apples and Jessica bought Emma some Grantham cakes and Brandy Snaps from a stall to which Emma seemed to find to irresistible not to keep returning to. Jessica rode on the new roundabout with Mary whilst Emma watched longingly.

The ride consisted of three groups of horses with brass poles, in the centre were models of musicians holding various instruments and seemingly playing them as the steam movement was in progress.

Jessica climbed up and sat as she had seen the ladies when the hunt had visited the hall, side saddle and gripping tightly to the brass pole. As the music started the whole contraption moved around in addition to which the horses moved up and down. Jessica was, at first terrified, but after a few moments had become confident enough to wave to Emma each time she came into view.

By nine o'clock, Jessica needed to leave Emma. She kissed her fondly on the cheek and hurried towards the High Street where Tom Jennings was waiting. As they reached the outskirts of the town they realised that what had begun as a mist one could barely discern, had now developed into a dense fog.

They slowly edged their way along the road, the horse with it's head down, the monotonous sound of its' hooves gently clip clopping along seemed to make the journey so much longer. The company, comprising of Jessica, Mary and Alice were peering into the mist, but were able to see nothing. The single lamp still alight seemed only to reflect back from the mist and light nothing in front of them. The girls sitting quietly huddled together for warmth. Eventually, Tom announced,' if we're ever to reach the hall tonight we'll have to take it in turns driving and leading the cart'. The roads' too difficult to see in these conditions I don't want the horse to be confused.

The journey was arduous, it was Mary's turn first. She took the lamp and was required to hold this up so that Tom could see it. The fog was so dense that the light could be seen no more than ten yards ahead. Twice she walked too close to the grass verge and twice Tom narrowly escaped getting the wheels of the cart stuck in the soft earth. The later it grew, the darker it grew. After a while Mary's arms were aching so much that she could no longer hold the lamp and the strain of peering into ever increasing darkness made her continually wander from side to side across the road. The cold night air had chilled her bones making it difficult to walk. Mary thankfully gave the lamp over to Jessica and walked cautiously to the cart fearful of falling into the holes that this stretch of road was notorious for.

CHAPTER 22

Jessica moved on steadily, she could now feel the extra chill of the mist coming up from the river, they had now taken so long to cover the journey to this point that the oil in the lamp was burning low and the flame was slowly dying. As they neared the bridge over the river Tom called for the horse to halt, and for Jessica to return to the cart.

'What's the matter', asked Jessica as she reached the cart.

'Sshh', said Tom, 'I thought I heard someone calling, listen'.

There it was again, splashing water and definitely a horse whinnying, then a voice crying for help, it was so faint as the mist was muffling all sounds. It was also difficult to gauge which side of the road the sound was coming from. From one side of the road the river was split into three separated by small islands, whilst the other side was the mill and the Millrace. The sound of water racing past the huge wooden wheel did nothing to help them.

Tom quickly detailed Mary to hold the horse steady whilst sending Alice, one of the housemaids across the road to listen. Jessica stood on the opposite side by the bridge, whilst Tom cautiously went towards the water on the same side as Jessica, because he was fairly certain this was the area he had first heard the sound.

When he had ascertained that everyone was in position he called:

'hallo, hallo there'

'help, please help', came a voice in response, a voice that was obviously weakening, the horse whinnied once again.

'where are you?' cried Tom

'I'm on the island, the horse is somewhere near the bank'

Tom called to the girls.

'Alice, come towards the water, I need a hand to steady me, Jessica see if we've got any rope in the cart, Mary, don't let that damned horse move a muscle'.

Tom, with the aid of Alice located the horse, it had slipped and was lying on its side held above the water only by its bridle, which had hooked itself on a branch of a tree, which had fallen in the recent October gales. He let go of Alice's hand and moved cautiously over the muddy bank towards the horse, which had once again regained enough strength to struggle.

'Whoa there, keep still you beast you' ordered Tom, 'Alice get back to the bank and see where the hell Jessica is with that rope, I pray to God there is some'.

The rope was not in the cart, Jessica had run her fingers over every inch of the inside and had collected several splinters for her trouble, but had found no rope. As Alice once again reached the cart, she had an idea.

'Let's take the reins off the horse, they'll be enough in the traces to hold. Mary you'll just have to hold the bridle, an we'll hobble him with bonnet ribbons.

This done, Alice and Jessica made their way towards Tom, he tied one end of the reins around his waist and after winding them around the base of the tree, gave the other end to the girls to hold, with the reins around the tree and the girls holding the reins held firm. The distance was short, but treacherous in the fog and darkness. Tom waded into the reeds that edged the river bank towards the horse, he did not want to startle the creature for fear of it kicking out and either hitting him and giving serious injury or injuring itself. Tom finally reached the horse and with soothing sounds and strokes managed to calm the panicked animal whilst attempting to unhook the strapped reins and hold onto them firmly. Once the tension was removed the horse scrambled to its feet. Tom had great difficulty holding on to him, he could feel the reins around his waist pull tighter and with this he could feel his breathing being constricted.

At last the horse was under control, Tom loosed him and allowed him to scramble up the bank, which he did unaided. Tom just had time to shout to Mary, but try as she might to catch it with a wild eyed frightened horse coming towards her, she only just managed to get out of the way before she was trampled under foot.

The horse galloped past her and disappeared down the road reins flying.

Mary pulled herself to her feet, and called to the others, they reassured her they were all right. After this little drama was past, they faced the real task of getting the rider across the river to safety. Tom knew the island was not far off and he was quite a good swimmer, but on a cold night, with poor visibility and the mill racing at full pace, could he risk it?'

He called to the person on the island, 'are you injured'?

'No, no I'm not, only cold and wet', called the man, he

did indeed sound so cold you could almost hear his teeth chattering.

'Well sir,' shouted Tom, 'I'm trying to think of a way to get you off before you go down with pneumonia'.

At last Tom hit upon an idea.

'Jess, go and ask Mary for the lamp, but don't relight it yet'.

Jessica found her way back to the cart and got the lamp.

'Here's the lamp Tom' she said.

'Good, now find a block of wood', said Tom confidently, 'a branch or something big enough to hold the lamp, whilst at the same time helping to support me in the water'.

Jessica could not find anything in the fog remotely matching Tom's requirements. In the end she had an idea, she clambered once more up the bank and with Mary's help managed to release the duckboard from the cart, she dragged this down the bank.

'Come on Jess', called Tom, 'is there no wood"?

'I've got it Tom, but it's heavy, I can only drag it', shouted Jessica totally out of breath.

'Good girl, even better than a branch', said Tom, when he saw what she had.

'Now Alice, your bonnet ribbons quick.

Alice took off her bonnet and tore the ribbons free, amidst a sudden gush of tears, she was cold, frightened and had only just managed to save enough for the purchase of the bonnet. Still sniffling, the young girl passed the ribbons to Tom, he quickly lashed the lamp to the side hooks of the duckboard.

'Now', he said, 'I'm going to edge along this tree, and tie the end of the reins to it, and tie the other end to my belt and swim , using the duck board for support towards the island. I know I won't get all the way, but at least with the lamp lit, the poor man over there will be able to see the light, an hopefully be able to wade out if he can and reach me.

'Oh no', cried Alice, now completely overcome with fear, 'don't Tom, don't what if, what if you're ohh'.

'Oh shut up', cried Jessica irritably.

'Hallo there' called Tom

'Hallo', came the call once more.

'Can you swim sir?' Tom shouted once again.

'Yes, yes but not far' called the man.

'I'm going to swim out towards the island, I'm lighting the lamp, I'll get as near to you as I can, but don't enter the water sir, until I've reached the full extent of my line, I'll tell you when that will be, but do make sure you've nothing on that can be an encumbrance to your progress'.

'I hear you' shouted the man.

Tom had trouble lighting the lamp, and after checking that Alice had returned to Mary and with Jessica's help, entered the water. The shock of the icy water took his breath and he clung tightly to the duckboard, initially not being able to move a muscle. He swam out towards what he hoped was the small island. When the full extent of the line was reached he called, 'sir, sir', but the effort of anymore was just too much, the cold and the fort of the swim were proving too difficult.

'Are you ready?' the man called.

'Yes, yes, I'm there now', called Tom and clung even more tightly to the board.

He heard a splash and after what seemed to be an absolute eternity felt a hand next to his on the board.

'Tight sir, hold tight' he said.

'Uh', was the only reply the man had the energy to reply.

They both began to swim back resting heavily on the board, so heavily in fact that the lamp was extinguished.

A scream was heard, it was Jessica, who had been straining her eyes, secure in the way she saw the light to reassure her of Tom's existence, now she could no longer see the light her confidence vanished. Tom heard the scream but was too exhausted to reassure her.

Jessica made her way to the road in tears, Mary and Alice also dissolved in tears as they spotted her, but their sobs were halted by the sound of a voice.

'Jess, where the hell are you?' the sound of the voice bought fresh tears as Jessica ran down the bank to see Tom and the Gentleman stripped to the waist, covered in mud and shivering on the bank. Mary, who had become nigh frozen to the spot with waiting left Alice with the horse, and made her way down to join Jessica. The girls took off their shawls and wrapped them around the shoulders of the two men and helped them to the cart. They climbed aboard and set off up the road with Alice walking and leading the now rein-less horse. It was only as Alice walked into a thorn hedge scratching her face did they know they had reached the fork in the road.

It was almost midnight as they were nearing the final stretch of road to the hall that they saw lights advancing towards them, as they drew near they heard a strong voice call.

'Anyone there?'

'Yes, yes,' called Alice, 'we're here'.

When the party drew near, it was a combined group of workers from the Hall estate, who had grown alarmed at the lateness of the party also with them was a party of workers from another estate close by who had become worried when their masters rider-less horse had returned.

CHAPTER 23

They all suffered from colds for the next week, but were fortunate to suffer nothing more.

One morning as Jessica came into the kitchen the young man who she had encountered before stood before her. She was initially annoyed, she thought that despite the fact the she had not told him where she worked, he had found this information and called to see her. In truth what had happened was, he was a worker on the estate of the gentleman they had assisted and had been sent with a reward of ten pounds each, a princely sum, but little compared with the man's life.

George Collins, which was the name of the man, had been as surprised to see Jessica, as she was to see him. He explained how his master had become stuck on the island, and question that had been asked by everyone involved, but had at the time been the least of their worries.

What had happened was the man was making his way slowly home, when his horse was spooked at the bridge, it had pulled down the bank and despite all his efforts it had careered towards the water throwing its master far into the water. He had become dazed and confused and could remember little until he heard the voices calling in response to his calls for help.

The little group were thrilled with their new found wealth, Alice replaced her bonnet and Jessica and Mary replaced their shawls, all put some money by. Tom bought a new suit and looked very handsome when he attended church the following Sunday.

CHAPTER 24

It seemed to Jessica that wherever she was, George Collins was also there. She had enquired a little about him and it appeared that he had the reputation of being a drunkard and was also known for his bouts of violence. She was worried about him and was strangely attracted to him, not that she felt any love for him, she knew that kind of love was reserved for James Conserton, she felt it was impossible to recreate that with anyone else, still, she was now thirty two years old and was getting concerned that she would end in the poor house a worn out old lady.

It was whilst she was out walking one day, that George seemingly appeared from nowhere, he walked along beside her, then stopped, grabbed both her hands in his huge rough ones and spun her around to face him.

'Marry me Jess, save me from myself, don't let me die from drink', he said in a despairing tone.

Jessica was so touched by this outburst that she was speechless. When she did speak, all she could do was to ask questions.

'And what if I said yes, would you not drink? 'What if I said yes, how would you provide for me?' What if I said yes, how long would it be before you deserted me and left me with nothing but the workhouse?'

'Jess', he said calmly, 'Jess, I promise I'd not drink, I know I could get a job at the new Railway company as a dray driver and they've got houses you can rent, that have been built for the purpose.'

'then you have to prove yourself, don't drink, don't fight and save money, don't bother me for one year and if you can do all these things I'll think about it'. She knew this was a very demanding set of rules, but was determined that she would marry only a strong minded man.

'Without you to keep me to these promises it's going to be difficult, but I'll try Jess, I promise I'll try', with that he let her hands free, checked his pocket watch and explained he must return to work. He left her and walked towards the estate where he worked, on the way he passed the public house, he smelled the beer and could hear his friends laughing and talking inside. He stopped, once again he took out his pocket watch, he shrugged his shoulders, then said, 'what the hell, she'll never know, I'll start my promise tomorrow', with that he crossed the road, pushed open the door and strode towards the bar, where the innkeeper had poured his beer as he saw him in the road.

Jessica meanwhile, heart pounding, not with love and excitement, but more with concern at what she had just done, marched quickly down the road and before she had realised just what she was doing had actually reached the town.

Jessica had recently received a letter from her sister Emma, there had been a change of plan, the farm had been sold and they had bought a small shop in the Market Street, the shop sold chocolate and boiled sweets, it was in a prime position as it was next to the entrance of the town theatre, anyone going to visit that theatre for a night out was almost certain to try some of their fancy foods during the show. In addition to this George Bassford had now become adapt at making his own boiled sweets, word soon got around and before long Emma was running to shop almost single handed whilst George made the sweets and visited local markets where he rented stalls to sell his goods. Of course no opportunity was allowed to pass so when the fair arrived in the town a stall was quickly erected and trading was always brisk.

Jessica decided to visit Emma not only to try the samples of her fare, but also to discuss with her what she thought would be the right decision regarding George Collins. Emma appeared worried on the news Jessica brought, she herself considered that it was almost impossible to save someone from themselves regarding drink and that Jessica should think very hard indeed before making such a momentous decision. Jessica left Emma also worried about her future, just what was she to do?

CHAPTER 25

The next few months were so busy that Jessica had no time to think of George Collins. Miss Geraldine's marriage to Paul Leeming was being organised and not only was part of the hall being decorated, but also the furniture needed checking and given a thorough polish, after which it needed a re-polish after the decorators had fully finished. The entrance to the hall was painted to resemble marble in various colours from beige through green to black. It really did look spectacular when it was completed. The invitation list was completed, and Jessica had started on embroidering a tablecloth as a wedding present, this along with the crochet antimacassars which she was also working on were to be a present from the whole of the staff.

The day of the wedding approached, all the servants were required to attend church, to sit or stand at the rear and to attempt not to be noticed by the guests. Whilst the happy couple were signing the register they quietly left in order so that they were in position on the steps of the hall as the happy couple arrived.

Geraldine looked beautiful, it was the onset of summer and she wore an off white dress of delicately woven silk with embroidered flowers the centre of each flower was a small cluster of seed pearls. Her hair was a thick braid entwined with orange blossom, the fragrance wafting as she moved her head. Her grandmother's silk veil on her head was held in place by a comb of tortoise shell decorated with silver and tiny diamonds. She carried herself with the utmost grace and looked totally radiant.

After the wedding due to the amount of guests staying at the hall, Jessica was required to assist in the turning down of the beds, as she entered the last room she was startled to see someone inside looking out of the window. The man had thrown his coat on the bed as the day had been warm.

'I'm sorry sir, I didn't realise anyone was here', said Jessica, beginning to re-open the door.

'Jessica, it's me, please close the door', it was James Conserton. Jessica was dumbstruck, she didn't realise he had attended the wedding and if she had, she would have made absolutely certain she did not enter his room. 'I'm sorry sir, but I really don't think'

'Just close the door Jessica, and please come over here', his voice was so gentle, but he had a sound of complete despair in it. She crossed the room, and stood by his side looking into his soft green eyes that complemented the soft golden colour of his hair, which reminded her of her favourite pale chrysanthemums.

'Sir' Jessica said, 'Sir, please I have no control over my emotions'.

James placed his hands on Jessica's shoulders to hold her steady. HE removed his right hand and placed it under her chin, tilting it up towards his face. Jessica closed her eyes, she couldn't bear to look into his eyes. He gently let the back of his hand move over her cheek and with a finger tip gently stroked first one, the other of her closed eyes. He reached down for her hand and gently lifted to his lips and kissed it several times, so very tenderly. Jessica leaned towards him and placed her head on his chest, she felt his arm encompass her waist, and her mind was in turmoil. She'd heard stories of gentlemen who took advantage of servants, only for the servants to be dismissed from service and have another mouth to feed in addition to their own.

She thought of George Collins, rough hands, course voice, beer soaked breath then she thought of the man holding her so tenderly. She knew without doubt that she must taste one moment of tenderness before committing herself to a life of hard work.

They moved towards the bed and sat down together. He placed his arms around her and kissed her tenderly. '

'Only if you really feel you want to Jessica' he said tenderly.

She didn't answer, he moved to unbutton the top of her high-necked blouse.

Suddenly he jumped as a knock on the door was heard. Jessica only just managed to stifle a loud exclamation.

'What is it?' he called

'May I turn down your bed sir'? came the voice of Alice

'It's already been done young lady' he replied.

'Sorry to disturb you sir'. She replied.

Jessica's heart was now pounding, not only with passion but also with fear. 'Sir, I must go sir, or I shall be missed' she was totally breathless.

'Oh Jessica, are we never to be together?'

'No sir, I don't think we are, but please, before I go, just kiss me goodbye, as you will see me no more'

She lifted her face to his and he kissed her, holding onto her long after the kiss had finished, her head resting on him, his arms holding her tightly.

'Goodbye sir', she said, 'I hope you'll be happy with some-one someday".

'Goodbye Jessica'.

She opened the door and slipped quietly out, she went up to her room and when at last she was alone threw herself on the bed and sobbed herself to sleep.

CHAPTER 26

A note arrived for Jessica from George Collins, it told her that he had managed to get a job as a drayman and also a house, but this only if he had a wife. The houses were a priority to couples and families as it would be unfair for single persons to hold three bed-roomed properties. Would Jessica therefore consider releasing him from the one year apart and marry him within the month.

Jessica thought long and hard about this and came to the conclusion that she was never to see James again and the long -term future looked bleak. The only alternative was to marry George and accept what she knew was a difficult future willingly.

Jessica wrote to George Collins one week later. She did not receive a reply by return due to the fact that he found this another occasion for celebration, got himself involved in a fracas and was jailed for one week after breaking the arm and nose of his opponent.

The wedding was arranged for January 12th 1897, a little longer wait than George had wanted, but then Jessica could not let her employers go short staffed at Christmas time. What should have been a time of excitement and pleasure gave way to one of despondency. Jessica could not stop thinking about what she was about to do, she hoped George Collins would benefit and keep his promise of abstinence, she hoped this in turn would prevent him from being violent. She knew he would never be tender, that was just not in his nature.

The idea of submitting to this man filled her with revulsion, she did in fact secretly hope for a short life after her marriage.

Her employers had told her she could return with no questions asked at any time, but she knew she would never admit defeat. No, her future was in her own hands and no one else.

CHAPTER 27

January 12th arrived at last, it was a cold day, there had been a heavy frost during the night and she had to break the ice from the water jug in her bedroom before she could wash.

After washing, she put on her clean clothes and made a neat parcel of her dirty ones with brown paper and string. This parcel, together with a box of odd pieces of crockery and a set of cutlery bought by the staff at the hall were two sets of sheets and two tablecloths which she had carefully embroidered in the months leading to the wedding, all would be taken to her new home by Tom Jennings after he had dropped her at the Salvation Citadel where she was to be married.

George, had, she thought bought a bed, table two chairs and a chest for their new home, paid for with money he faithfully put by as he promised. In reality they had been purchased with a loan from his new employers, to be paid back alongside his rent for the property, leaving barely enough for food each week.

Mary had been given time off from her duties to attend the

wedding and would return with Tom after the wedding.

As they travelled along the road to the town, Mary chattered, reminding Jessica of the times they had had together, of the night of the fair as they passed over the bridge. As they were nearing the Citadel, Mary grasped Jessica's hand squeezing it as re-assurance not only for Jessica but also for herself.

'Jessica, I don't know this man and I'm sure you like him, but are you sure you know what you're doing?' she asked with an anxious look on her face. 'It's not too late to come back to people who love you, you know"

'I'll be alright once we've both settled down, so long as he keeps his promise to keep off the drink'. Jessica said looking at the hem of her skirt and picking imaginary pieces of dirty from it.

'Well I've never known a real drinker to give up for anyone Jessica, truly I never have', said Mary, 'but I can see you're determined, so I'll just wish you the best of luck and say no more about it.'

As they reached the Citadel, Jessica could see George waiting, stamping his feet in the cold. His greeting was not the best a bride could wish for on her wedding day.

'Cum on, cum on, it's freezing out here', then looking at Mary and smiling, continued,' introduce me to this cumly gel then'.

Jessica introduced Mary, both women turned to each other and both bit their bottom lips, Mary could not resist whispering.

'You sure?' to Jessica, who replied with a simple nod of the head.

The wedding proceeded without further adieu and the couple along with Mary and George's friend Jack left the Citadel. Jessica's family did not attend as they were now involved with young families of their own. Journeys were therefore very difficult for them all.

The wedding over Jessica thought they would return to the house where she knew food had been prepared by Mary and set out by Tom who had also lit the fire.

'Off we go then, let's celebrate. I've got a table for us at the Oak', said George, slapping Jack on the shoulder.

'Yes', said Jack. 'I could do wi sumat warm inside me'.

'But, you promised George', said Jessica, 'and Mary has prepared food for us back at the house'.

'An you promised Jess' said George tersely, ' to obey, get off then Jack 'n' me will see you later', with that they walked towards the 'Oak".

Jessica stood at the doorway to the Citadel, on that cold winter day, arms held loosely by her side and let the tears fall, Mary said nothing.

After a few minutes she wiped away her tears on the back of her hand took a deep breath, shrugged her shoulders and announced

'Come on Mary, Tom will have eaten everything in sight if we're much later', slipped her arm in Mary's and began to walk in the direction of new home.

As they reached the door Tom threw it open to greet them,. When he saw only the two women his smile faded from his face, he was unsure just what had happened. Had Jessica had a change of mind, had he not turned up?

It was Mary who broke the silence,

'he's gone to the boozer with his mate to celebrate the capture, I'm sorry Jessica, but I feel really bitter against this man of yours'.

'Let's get inside, we don't want the neighbours to gossip before we move in do we'? said Jessica ushering them inside and closing the front door.

Once inside she once again burst into tears, after two hours and still no sign of George, Mary and Tom needed to leave. They had to return to their duties at the Hall.

Jessica made up the fire and sat beside it listening to the clock ticking the hours by. At four in the afternoon she lit the lamp, at nine in the evening she extinguished the flame, lit the candle after damping down the fire and climbed the stairs. She undressed and slipped between the cold sheets, exhausted by the emotion of the day she fell asleep.

CHAPTER 28

An hour later she was awakened by a noise in the street below, accompanied by a hammering on the door. Jessica got out of bed, wrapped the blanket around her and felt her way down the stairs, through the living room and front parlour to the door, her bare feet felling icy on the cold floor.

She unbolted and unlocked the door and saw George, face twisted with inebriation, breath stinking of a mixture of beer and spirits, holding onto the jamb of the door for support.

Jessica stepped aside and let him stagger over the threshold and closed the door behind him. Once inside in the pitch black, he swung his arms to find the wall, in doing this, his arm caught Jessica in the face, knocking her off balance. Jessica scrambled to her feet, terrified, she had never known such terror, she made her way to the door, hitting her knee on it in her haste. She pulled the door closed behind her, leaving the now prone George to sleep off his drunkenness on the cold floor. She herself went back to bed where she once again cried out the day's events until she could cry no more. She eventually slept until she heard the hooter from the local factory announce to the inhabitants of the town that it was six thirty, and that they had half and hour to reach their place of work.

Jessica got out of bed and after lighting the lamp went down stairs, she lit the lamp and raked out the fire preparing to light another, she touched her face and winced, it was obviously bruised, she hoped it wasn't a bruise that showed, because she would need to go to the corner shop for some provisions.

It was then she heard the door being opened and saw George stagger into the living room, beard beginning to grow, clothes dishevelled and reeking.

'I've been sick in there, you'd best clean it up before you get mi breakfast', he announced, 'and while we're at it you'll have to rise earlier it's cold in here, you need to light that fire before I rise'

With that he walked through the living room, picked up a bucket from the scullery, unlocked the back door and went to the yard pump to draw water for a wash.

Jessica, angry with him, but not daring to confront him, lit the fire, breaking the firewood with such vigour that she was only prevented from completely splintering the wood due to the pain from her knee injury from the previous night. She lit the fire and took the bread from the previous evening from the cupboard, bread that should have been consumed at the wedding breakfast, but which was in fact to be eaten at a very different breakfast indeed.

When the fire was hot, Jessica got out the toasting fork, which had been a present from her brother Thomas and his wife. She spiked the bread and held it close to the flame. After the toast was ready she buttered it and poured the freshly boiled water from the kettle to the teapot.

George came into the room and sat at the table, he ate his way through the toast and drank two cups of tea before saying:- 'you've got black on your face, go and wash it off'.

"I would if I could', said Jessica tersely , 'but it's not black, dirt, or anything else, that's my wedding present from you when you were blind drunk', with that she walked quickly into the scullery and went herself to get water from the pump.

George replaced his cup on the table, put both elbows on the table, sunk his head into his hands, he couldn't remember a thing about the previous evening, the only thing he knew was that he hadn't slept in the bed and therefore had not even consummated the marriage. As far as the bruise on Jessica's face, he had no idea of how such a thing happened, but if she said he had done that then he must have done so.

When Jessica came back into the room he arose and crossed to where she was standing by the range. He put both his strong arms around her as her back was towards him, he felt her whole body tense.

'I've broken my promise Jess I'm sorry, I don't know what possessed me, but when I get home from work we'll do what we should have done last night'.

The Genie with turban in Markfield Hospital - Eric before his operation.

George Jr.
approximately 14 years old

George Jr.
approximately 80 years old.

Flo and George Snr.

George Snr. before his accident

Lillian Collins

Jessica & George
in Skegness

Flo - on left

Flo (2nd from left), Louise Collins (3rd from left)

• *Joan Morey*

A 1st World War postcard

Lillian & George Trueman Collins

114

George Jnr married Nancy after Jessica's death.

George Jnrs Birth Certificate

Empress Road, Judges Street, Thomas Street
Victory in Europe celebrations

CHAPTER 29

George went to work and Jessica got down to the jobs in hand, baking bread, cooking the meal for the evening, washing the clothes she had no time to wash before she left the hall. Alone she was happy, but as the time grew close for his return Jessica began to feel nervous.

George's footstep could be heard by about six in the evening in the entryway, which led to the rear entrance of the house. He opened the gate to the yard and eventually the backdoor. George entered the scullery and hung his coat on the nail, which was driven into the back door. He then picked up the bowl and carried it to the range where he drew off hot water.

'Dinner ready Jess?' he asked as he entered the room.

'Yes', was the only reply she made.

'Good, I'll just wash mesen then I'll sit down,

Jessica picked up the boiling kettle and filled the large brown teapot.

After George had washed he came into the room and sat at the table. Jessica placed the large stew-pot in the centre of the table and sat down to join her husband. She bowed her head to give thanks, but noticed he hadn't time for such niceties. They ate in silence and Jessica cleared the table, tidied up and took out her sewing. The clock ticked noisily, and eventually George broke the silence.

'Sorry gel, it's not a very good start to the rest of your life is it?'

'No George it's not a start at all', she said, not lifting her head from her embroidery.

CHAPTER 30

By nine o'clock George rose, 'come on gel, I'll lock up, you damp the fire, it's time we went up'.

The time had come; the time Jessica had been dreading all day. She rose and did as he asked. She lit the candle and went up before he had finished his jobs. Jessica undressed quickly and climbed into bed pulling the covers tightly around her.

After a while she felt the bed sink to one side as George climbed into the bed beside her. He coughed, she did not respond. He turned over to the side facing Jessica's back, kissed the nape of her neck and spoke,

'Come on gel, you can't hold off forever', he put his hands on her shoulders and rolled her onto her back. Jessica's heart was pounding so much that George's words were almost drowned.

George moved his hands over her body, but the only thing she could think of was how rough his hands were on her flesh, no one had ever touched her body before.

After George had made love to her he rolled over onto his side without a word and was soon snoring loudly.

Jessica was now certain that George had not waited until he was married and now regretted that she and James had not consummated their love.

CHAPTER 31

The weeks passed and Jessica discovered just what she had done, with little money for food she placed a notice in the window of the corner shop and before long was taking in washing from her neighbours. The house was full of wet clothes on lines drying overnight, and when the washing was dry the smell of steam on clean clothes pervaded the whole house.

Jessica was feeling continually tired. George had not been for a drink since their wedding day and was, for the most part, if not romantic at least attentive.

After six months not only had they managed to pay off most of their debts, but had also put a little money by for more furniture.

George had dug the small garden and they had already had their first picking of peas.

It was late one warm summer evening that George announced he was going out for a drink with Jack.

'I'll only have one gel, an I won't be late'.

Jessica knew this promised would not, could not be kept.

When George returned Jessica was in bed, he entered the house and Jessica could hear him bumping into the furniture and cursing. He made his way upstairs, still muttering to himself, undressed, struggling with his trousers and not bothering to take off his shirt. He pulled out the pot from under the bed and relieved himself, belched loudly and eventually climbed into bed.

Jessica felt a sense of relief as she felt him settle down to sleep, but it seemed the moment his head hit the pillow, he was awake and sober, it was on this night, a night of rough lovemaking that she conceived her first child. She had wanted the conception to be memorable in a totally different way to this.

Jessica could not understand why she was always tired. Of course, she had a great deal of washing and ironing, but it did pay the bills. She had recently bought a chaise lounge for the living room. It was from Mr. Jones shop and although he had had it for some time he assured Jessica the wood was sound with no worm and the black hide upholstery looked as though it had in the past very little wear.

It was not until she could no longer button her skirt that Jessica realised she was pregnant. She worried a great deal over this, as she was uncertain how long she could continue to do such volumes of washing and what if she died and the child survived, how would it live, who would care for it? Certainly not George, she knew he would immediately return to his old ways, without a second thought for his child.

'Stop it', she said to herself, 'shake yourself up Jessica stop feeling sorry for you'.

She didn't tell George about the baby and it wasn't until he said one night,

'Jess, your putting on weight, you look like the side of a

house side on, that she announced:

'I'm expecting your baby George Collins, so don't worry me', with that she rose and went upstairs to bed. She couldn't understand her action, he'd said nothing to offend yet she'd spat out the words to him and left.

He, in turn was confused, what was the matter with the woman, anyone would think having a baby was something new, all the same, it meant extra responsibility, extra money, he just hoped it was worth it, at least it could look after him in his old age.

He locked up, damped down the fire and went up to bed. Jessica was lying with her back towards him.

'Come on Jess, roll over', he said, 'I want to talk about the baby'.

Jessica rolled over and gave him a long hard look.

'What do you want to say?' she said in a matter of fact way.

'When's it due Jess, how far gone are you, I mean how long a wait is left?'

'Four months from now we'll have an extra mouth to feed, four months extra clothes, extra time, an you, never giving me enough to live on now'.

'I'll look after you both Jess, I will, I made a promise and one thing I do keep is that kind of promise gel, for the rest of my life, I'll look after you'.

Jessica turned her back to George, desperately wanting to believe him, but deep down knowing that even if he wished this he was too weak willed to uphold all his promises,

The following evening Jessica tried to make amends by cooking George his favourite lamb hot pot, and suet pudding. She washed her hair and put a small vase of flowers freshly picked from the garden on the table, the flowers were the first snowdrops land it was a week before Christmas. Jessica looked at the clock, six fifteen:

'So much for your promises' said Jessica out loud, '; you couldn't even keep it for one day George'

Nine o'clock came, she heard George's footsteps in the entry, heard the gate, then the back door open and close.

George shouted, 'Jess, Jess is my dinner still alright?'

Jessica couldn't understand it, he didn't sound drunk, he didn't sound angry, and he did sound happy. George entered the living room, he smiled, and Jessica looked at him strangely.

'Where have you been?' She had wanted to sound angry, but when she saw him her anger subsided.

'I've been doing extra time Jess, we'll need to buy some things for the baby won't we?'

Jessica couldn't believe what she was hearing, she smiled and moved towards the oven to get the lamb from it, it was still fine, as she had been adding a little water occasionally so that the gravy didn't dry out.

They ate in near silence, he was tired and hungry, so hungry in fact that he hadn't washed before he sat down. After he had eaten he leaned back in his chair and patted his full stomach.

'I knew I married you for something' he said smiling 'you're a wonderful cook Jess.'

'Is that it then?' Jessica answered feeling once again injured, not daring to trust his mood.

'No, no Jess'

She poured his tea and was just pushing his large cup of tea towards him when he leaned forward and grasped her small hand between both of his.

'Jess', he said, 'Oh Jess, I know I've not started well, but Oh

Jess, thank you, thank you for the baby, it's the first thing in my whole life that no one can ever take away from me. I'll be its father, no one else in the whole world, he'll be mine all mine'.

'I think I've got a little to do with it, I'm not just a place for it to rest you know', she laughed.

Poor George, it seemed he could never say the right thing.

'Jess, I really mean it, I'll work, I'll try to stop drinking and hitting out, notice this time, it's not a promise to stop, and it's a promise to try'.

'I noticed,' said Jessica, 'and I'll try to trust you a little more',

With that she that she rose and began to clear the table, George got up, still seemingly happy and went to the scullery for a bucket, he drew off some hot water from the range and returned to wash himself.

They sat, one each side of the fire. Jessica reading a book, George, puffing gently on his pipe, occasionally cleaning the stem with a pipe cleaner, the clock ticked on.

George rose and moved towards Jessica, he put his arm around her shoulder.

'I'll mek you a cup of tea eh gel, then it's up to bed for you, till you have that baby of ours it's early to bed, and I'll do the work down here, I'll damp the fire, an lock up, go on gel, as soon as you've finished that tea I'm making for you, go an get some beauty sleep, you've got to look after yourself for two people now.'

Jessica looked up at him, had his eyes softened? Did he really mean what he said?

'Thank you George, I know I've never felt so tired, I do need extra rest'.

'Jess', he said gently, 'Jess, I love you".

She smiled at him; he had never said that before, perhaps this baby would make a new man of him, who knows.

CHAPTER 32

George continued to work long hours, and Jessica carried on taking in volumes of washing. She was becoming very tired, whenever she sat down the baby would
begin to wriggle around, and it seemed that every-time she
lay down she became so uncomfortable she could not get to
sleep.

Christmas was over; it had been a much happier Christmas that she had envisaged. George had been making a delivery to a local farmer on Christmas Eve and the farmer having
had an excellent day at the local market had been celebrating early. George knocked on the door with the delivery; the
farmer's wife had opened the door and called her husband
to assist George in unloading the large box. When they had
finished the farmer said,

'Just a minute, it's Christmas tomorrow, what have you got
to eat?'

George told him they had managed to buy a small piece of
pork and the farmer said,

'Wait a minute',

He disappeared into the scullery and returned presenting George with a huge fat goose.

'I've had a good day at the market, this is one left over, take it and enjoy it'.

That year had been memorable for its good food.

January and February had been cold, very cold, it had snowed and the snow had lain on the ground for weeks. Jessica ventured outdoors very carefully, her boots were worn and the trampled snow on the paths was treacherous because the frost combined with the many feet over it had actually turned those paths into near sheets of ice. She was lucky she never actually slipped over.

The end of March drew near; Jessica knew it must almost be time for the baby to be born. On 31st March, Jessica was wading her way through the huge pile of ironing, on one of the first fine windy days of the year, when she felt a numb pain. She shook her head as if to clear it and carried on ironing. A while later another pain, then another and another. She knew this was the first warning sign of the impending birth. Jessica placed her iron on the hob and cleared the ironing blanket from the table. She tidied away her washing and popped labels on the individual piles of ironing. Another pain, she held onto the back of the chair until it was over. Jessica carried on tidying the house, intermittently surrendering to the surges of pain as they occurred more regularly.

When she had completed her tasks, she went next door, she tapped urgently on the door and Mrs. Upton answered the door. She only needed to glance at Jessica to know what her problem was.

'Up to bed gel, I'll fetch Mrs. Smith'.

Mrs. Smith was the local midwife. Jessica returned to her house and made her way slowly and clumsily up to bed. She

127

undressed in the cold room and lay on top of the bed too tired and exhausted to climb under the covers. She glanced at the clock, it was four fifteen in the afternoon, in two hours George would be home for tea and she hadn't got round to preparing it.

Mrs. Upton opened the door, crossed the room to the door to the stairs and Jessica heard her footsteps coming to the bedroom.

Jessica was in the throes of another contraction; Mrs. Upton crossed the room and grasped Jessica's hand. Jessica squeezed it tightly, gradually relaxing the pressure as the pain subsided.

Mrs. Upton was in her mid thirties, she had four children of her own, her first child had been born when she was eighteen and she was therefore able to leave the care of the family in her daughter's capable hands whilst she assisted Jessica.

'Mrs. Smith will be here by six thirty Jess, just take it easy gel' she said gently as yet another pain surged through Jessica's body. When this had subsided, Jessica gasped breathlessly,

'What if I can't hold on that long?'

'You've got hours to go yet lovey', said Mrs. Upton gently, 'an at your age it takes longer, after all you're no spring chicken are you?"

CHAPTER 33

Six fifteen came and George's footsteps could be heard as usual in the entry. Tom Upton had arrived earlier, so Jessica knew it was George. As soon as he entered the house he sensed something was wrong. For one thing there was no smell of food. He crossed the room, opened the stair door and called up the stairs.

'Jess, Jess are you alright?'

It was Mrs. Upton, who appeared at the top of the stairs,

'Her times come George, there's some food next door, just you be off now, we'll call you when you're needed'.

George touched the tip of his cap and without a word turned, left the house and went to see Tom Upton.

The time passed, Mrs. Smith arrived as promised and after checking Jessica progress went downstairs, leaving Mrs. Upton to keep Jessica company.

Once downstairs Mrs. Smith made up the fire, until a good blaze was itself lighting up the living room. She then climbed the stairs with a bucket filled with coal, kindling and paper for lighting a fire in the bedroom grate.

'We don't want the poor little things entering this world and wishing e never had, due to the cold do we".

She posed the question to Jessica, who at the time could not answer.

The time ticked on and Jessica's contractions became more and more frequent. By eleven fifty five she had begun pushing and by twelve fifteen Mrs. Smith announced that the head could clearly be seen. By twelve twenty one more push produced a very loud, very healthy looking baby girl.

'Nearly all over now dear', said Mrs. Smith, as Mrs. Upton was by now wrapping up the baby, clearing it's mouth, nose and eyes and handing her to her exhausted mother.

Jessica lay on her side, baby cradled in the crook of her arm, sweat still standing on her brow.

'Hello, little one', she said gently stroking the child's face with one finger, 'I'm your Mam, and I promise to love you forever'.

Jessica lay back on her pillow completely drained of energy after the evening's events.

Mrs. Upton had gone next door to give the good news of the safe arrival of the baby to George, whilst Mrs. Smith cleared up and arranged the room so as to look as if the baby had arrived miraculously with no fuss or bother.

By the time George came into the room, it looked as if there had never been the drama of a birth, and the baby girl lay tightly wrapped and asleep in the crib that Emma had loaned Jessica.

George exhibiting anything but confidence, entered the room, he looked at Jessica.

'Hello gel, I gather you didn't have too bad a time then, an it's a gel, well never mind, you've plenty of time to get me a lad, an I'm sure it won't bi long'.

George had never been known for his tact, he crossed to where the child lay, looked at it and eventually touched the tiny head.

'What shall we call her then?'

'I've been thinking', said Jessica, 'whilst my pains were bad, all I could think of were that sermon that Jesus gave about the lilies, you know, consider the lilies of the field. Shall we call her Lillian?'

'Lillian', George mulled the name over, 'Lillian, that'll do nicely, yes, Lillian Collins, nowt wrong wi that is there?'

Lillian Collins was born on 1st April 1898, a child who was to be the first to George and Jessica. A year passed fairly uneventfully with the exception of George once more bowing to temptation and getting roaring drunk, but he had in his opinion good cause for celebration, after all he had just become a father hadn't he!

After that episode Jessica once more became quiet when George was around, her work was even harder as George had only said he would help until the baby was born and this was all he did do.

The baby was lovely, she had deep brown eyes and when her hair began to grow it was dark brown and had a slight curl to it. She seemed a bright little thing and by three months was gurgling away as if she knew exactly was she was talking about.

One morning, just as Jessica had risen, she felt violently sick, she ran to the privy outside. As she returned to the house feeling weak, she heard the baby cry. It was a cold October day and Jessica had wanted to light the fire before she had brought the baby down, she could still hear George snoring away upstairs, and did not want him awakened, either by Lillian, or before the fire was lit, as either would, she knew, start the day on an unpleasant note.

She went quickly up the stairs and took the baby from her crib; the baby was hot and very red faced. Jessica felt her forehead, the baby had a temperature. She took little Lillian downstairs and fed her, this quietened her, but as Jessica lay her down she seemed listless.

Jessica was concerned, perhaps the baby had the same thing that made her sick. She quickly lit the fire and put the kettle on to boil.

The baby whimpered, Jessica picked her up again saying,

'there, there sweetheart, just be good while I get your Dad's breakfast, then we'll have a cuddle when he's gone to work.'

She propped little Lillian up in the corner of the chaise lounge. But she flopped back.

After George had risen and been seen off to work, Jessica set about changing and dressing the baby. It was then she noticed the rash; the baby's body was covered in a red rash of tiny spots. Jessica panicked, she held Lillian close to her, there had been reports of Scarlet Fever in the town and Lillian was so very young. She kept the child cool by continually bathing her in lukewarm water, and by the evening the rash looked brighter than ever, when George arrived home there was no food ready, just a very tired and upset Jessica and a crying baby.

At first he was going to complain, until he saw his baby daughter, George made himself and Jessica some food and moved over to where she sat cradling the baby, Jessica had fallen asleep. He felt her head and whispered to his exhausted wife.

'Jess, Jess, I think the fever's broken, she's sleeping peacefully, it must have been one of those little things they get now and then, feel Jess, just feel her'.

Jessica touched the child gently; she was cool and yes, was indeed sleeping peacefully. Jessica smiled,

'I think you're right, I'll take her upstairs, can you warm her cot first, but not too much'.

George removed the warm brick from the range and carried it upstairs where he warmed the cot. He called to Jessica who carried the baby upstairs, she lay peacefully asleep and they both gazed at their daughter. George broke the silence,

'Come on, let's eat, I've not been slaving over a hot stove for nothing'.

He put his arm on Jessica's shoulders and she smiled.

After they had eaten, Jessica was telling George how she had thought initially they both had the same sickness, when George said,

'You're sure your not pregnant again Jess?'

Jessica looked up, almost afraid to face the truth, she had been trying to push this to the back of her mind, but her clothes had once again been getting tighter.

'Well, I don't know what we're going to do George, I think you're right, how are we going to manage, one is difficult enough.'

'Look at others' was George's reply, 'they all seem to manage, we'll get by, we're both healthy.

CHAPTER 34

Jessica produced a baby boy early the following May, much to the delight of George. They called the baby Wilfred. The labour was long and very difficult and it had taken Mrs. Smith some time to get the infant to breath properly. A week after the birth George was once again late home from work. Jessica braced herself for another scene when eventually arrived home, but at seven thirty there was a knock at the door, it was Jim Packe, he removed his cap as Jessica answered the door and she immediately became worried.

'Hello Jess', he said, 'I've got some bad news, George is at the doctor's house, he's not too bad, but the hoist slipped an a box he was lowering onto the cart slipped, he's broke a couple of fingers and got a nasty gash on his hand. I'm afraid he won't be working for a couple of weeks. I must get off home myself now or my wife will be worrying, bye Jess, see you soon'.

Jessica had no time to say anything; she stood in the doorway stunned. 'Bye Jim', was all she could say. She went into the living room and sat down, she rocked the tiny baby in his cradle, as Lillian pulled herself up on Jessica's skirt and rested her head on her mother's knee.

"I don't know how we'll manage this time, I'll have to try to earn more, but at least your Dad can watch the both of you while I get on can't he?'

They did manage, just, but they had to defer the payment of the rent until George returned to work and once again they were plunged into debt. There was, it seemed no way out of the trap they were in and apart from the fact that Jessica loved her babies dearly, there were times in Jessica's hard life when she did wish with all her heart that she was back at the Hall, with a little to spend and a warm house to move around in. There were also times when she closed her eyes and thought of James, but strangely she could no longer visualise him and she was thinking of him less and less.

CHAPTER 35

James Conserton had heard of Jessica's marriage and of the birth of her daughter. He still could not get Jessica out of his mind.

The newspapers were reporting the fact that the Boar's would not give franchise to those people who had left their homes and families to work the gold mines. The Boars referred to these as Uitlanders. The Uitlanders worked the mines and contributed a great deal to the economy of South Africa. They now out numbered the Boars but still had no rights. The situation was becoming very difficult. Many read the reports in England, but South Africa seemed a whole lifetime away and although they were shocked at the injustice did not feel it was truly their argument.

By 1894 the situation was becoming impossible, 35000 Uitlanders signed a petition that was sent to the Raat, the Parliament of the Boars. The Uitlanders now outnumbered the number of male Boars in the country.

Some liberal members of the Raat actually thought they might have a case, on such member a Mr. Jeppe, who was elected spokesman for the liberals said

" They own half the soil, they pay at least three quarters of the taxes". He went on to say "They are men who in capital, energy, and education are at least our equals. What will become of us or our children on that day when we may find ourselves in a minority of one in twenty without a single friend among the other nineteen, among those who made them strangers to the republic?"

Their appeal was still unsuccessful; they therefore turned to their countries of origin to aid them in their appeal.

The newspapers continued to report the disagreements between the South African Boar Republics of the Transvaal and the Orange Free State by October 9th 1899 a 48-hour ultimatum had been issued to Britain. Britain, however, had no intention of relinquishing their interest in gaining power over the gold mines at Witwatersrand. By October 26th an order had been issued to Britain and some of its colonies to recruit for a war in South Africa involving both republics. The Cape Colony was invaded also Natal state, these were both under the control of the British. The Boars attacked the three cities of Kimberley, Ladysmith and Mafeking.

It was at this point that James Conserton decided to leave his post in the Civil Service and to join the British forces to aid their pursuance for the rights of their erstwhile countrymen.

As James packed the few possessions he was taking with him, he wondered whether he would ever see his homeland again. He knew he would never be able to see Jessica. He put this to the back of his mind and carried on packing, placing his black leather bound Bible on the top of his luggage.

The journey by boat took about a month; on this journey James was initially sea sick, spending hours lying flat in his bunk, wondering why he had begun such a foolhardy adventure.

Nothing had prepared James for the searing heat, the constant noise of people who seemingly all chattered at once, the horses, the artillery, the accommodation, the wagons, all loaded with their supplies ranging from food to guns and rounds of ammunition.

The latrines were simply holes in the ground, the smell of human excreta, horse manure and cattle dung intermingled provided ones nose with such an intense mixture of smells, that until one got used to this. James felt in constant danger of being physically sick and the feeling of nausea brought him out in a hot sweat that seemingly had nothing to do with the heat. He leaned against the stoop that was the general's accommodation until told to move by the adjutant in charge.

The battalion to which James had been assigned as Captain was ordered to march into the bush, whereby they would eventually arrive at Belfast fort. The Boars had previously carried out an attack on the post. The position of the southern part of the fort was held and eventually after a vicious battle the Boars abandoned their advance and left the fort. Both sides had fought gallantly.

The Battalion camped by the river. For even the most hardy of men occasionally contracted dysentery. This journey was to be no exception as they were held up for a week in order that the weakened men might recover. The going was hard, the terrain sparse, mostly covered in bush dried golden by the burning sun. The men camped in their conical tents four men to a tent, sleeping toe to toe. It was hot, cramped and provided a smell that even the best could ill hide.

Each evening as they pulled up for a meal and rest. The

supplies wagons pulled up into an oblong as that used by the Boars, this provided some protection against attack.

Time permitting, James would move to a quiet area of the camp where, he would read his Bible and watch the beautiful spectacle of the setting sun over the veld until the sun disappeared over the horizon and the sky became blood red as the last vestiges of the suns glorious light faded quickly to give nothing but pitch black skies, and the evening became too cold, he would then retire to his tent to rest.

James saw death as no man should ever see. The incredible cruelty on either side, the abandonment of sick and injured to encounter death by the searing sun, the ants or wild animals that invaded the area. It was later after another battle that James, being one of the fortunate ones was taken prisoner by the Boars and marched to Pretoria where he joined other officers in a camp on the racecourse. The camp at night was surrounded by electric lights, which gave very few the opportunity of escape. The camp was comfortable by likes of other camps, there was water and food, which was given, the quality being good by the standards they had previously endured. He was astonished however, by the rudeness and abruptness with which the other officer captives related to their captors. James knew that it was his duty to attempt escape; he also knew that there seemed little reason to risk his life in doing so. After all, what was the use of a dead soldier? He spent many waking hours thinking and planning his escape but his plans were thwarted when the place where they were held prisoner was changed. It was luxurious by most standards, even sporting a gymnasium and a set of tennis courts. As one of the newspaper reports to reach Britain explained,

'The moment his enemy surrenders he become his guest, and the Boars certainly provided much better accommodations for the officers than those to which their own men are accustomed either in the field or at home.'

James was, by now a good deal thinner and becoming prematurely grey haired. He had spent now some six months in captivity, and although well cared for, he was still a prisoner. He had begun to organise small Christian services and Bible readings, but the numbers attending were small. The officers preferring to harass the women and girls who needed to pass on their way. Eventually a petition was sent and the officers and James along with is fellow officers were removed once again this time to a place, which was far less salubrious.

The camp was surrounded by barbed wire, and now had none of the luxuries they had previously known. It was at this time that James began to feel ill. He had been to visit an officer who was not well he would read the Bible with him. The medic had thought the officer had succumbed to the bites of mosquitoes and given him a particularly severe type of malaria.

Shortly after one of his visits to the officer James was running a temperature and was feeling very weak. Soon after initially feeling ill the medic was called, who suggested he remove to the camp hospital where James could be carefully watched. The medic suspected a severe case of dysentery. James died two days later, what was at first diagnosed as dysentery proved to be typhoid; the officer who James had attended had died the day before James. It wasn't long before more men went down with the disease.

The camp was burned and the men moved to what was hopefully a healthier place, but, with so many crowded together there was little wonder that the water would be contaminated.

In his belongings, which were sent back to his family was

a note, it simply said,

'Send my Bible to Jessica, she's the one who I feel would care for it as she would have cared for me if life had been fairer to the two of us'.

CHAPTER 36

George was, by now complaining of his lack of in-
volvement with the men he worked with and was
not appearing home before ten on a Friday evening. Jessica
knew that the work was arduous and that the men he worked
with were in the habit of going to the Inn straight after work,
but most of them didn't get violent after a few pints, George
did. Several times in recent weeks George had returned home
with cuts to his face and hands and on two occasions had
carried on attacks at home, leaving crockery broken and one
chair with a leg smashed which he repaired the following
day. Apart from the fact that George seemed now to be drinking more regularly, he was also spending money they could
ill afford. When she could stand it no longer, she took to
meeting him from work, taking his pay packet and giving
him enough for only two pints of beer, she was not alone in
this respect as a number of George's colleagues were also re-
ceiving similar treatment. George appeared to need his beer
regularly and when he returned home from work was now
insisting Jessica take a jug to the 'Beer Off' (Off Licence) at

the corner of the next street to theirs and have it filled, this now became a daily chore.

It was soon after he returned from work in August when little Lillian was three years old and Wilfred was two years old, that the heavily pregnant Jessica set out to collect George's beer. As she turned the corner, she slipped and fell awkwardly. Jessica felt the cold wet sensation of the beer seeping around her shoulder. She looked around but there was no one in sight, the day was hot, the evening had that smell of raw sewage that often accompanied the hot days of summer complete with the flies which seemd to have invaded their land. She had great trouble to getting up and to her feet; at last she managed to get to her feet and rested against the wall of a house to retain her composure. The jug was chipped, but fortunately had not broken. Fearing the wrath of her husband she decided to carry on with her task. On returning to the house, the first thought on George's mind was that she had taken rather a long time

"Have you been chatting instead of getting on with your job?' George asked angrily.

"I slipped, it took me some time to get up from the ground'

'It's a good job you didn't break the jug then, or you would have been even longer'.

It wasn't long before the pains began Jessica asked George to call Mrs. Smith, he was less than amused as now, not only was he to lose his hour of relaxed drinking, but would be required to sit with Mr. Smith or Mr. Upton, and wait. Two hours later Jessica produced another son, she called him Matthew, and he was a healthy weighty child.

CHAPTER 37

L ife continued, it was as Jessica had suspected her future to be when she married George Collins, difficult, but the children were healthy and happy so Jessica was thankful. She continued to take in washing and was now doing a little sewing and mending for the Hall. When Mary visited she always brought a little more work and it was collected by Tom when he was in town calling for provisions, at the same time he brought food which Mary had carefully wrapped, this always included luxuries such as fruit cake and muffins left over from the previous day at the Hall.

Mary handed Jessica a parcel wrapped in brown paper.

'I've been told to give this to you Jess, I think it's something that been sent especially for you, but they sent it to the Hall not knowing you'd left.'

After Mary had left Jessica unwrapped the parcel, in it she found James's Bible, she unfolded the letter accompanying it read it carefully, it simply said,

Please accept this Bible it belonged to our son James, his last wish was that you keep it close to you. James unfortunately died six months ago in an Officers prison camp in Pretoria.

Jessica sat down and held the Bible close to her; she then threw the letter in the fire so as George would never know to whom the book had belonged. She then said quietly to the air,

'I'll never let this out of my sight, it's a token of our respect'.

It was now 1901, initially the country had been joyful in the news that the Boar War was drawing to an end, but then tinged with sadness as news of the Queen's illness became widely known.

As her Majesty Queen Victoria passed away, the whole country was thrown into mourning, everyone who could afford it donned black for the time of the funeral. The main topic of conversation was what would the new King be like.

On the day of the funeral the newspapers were edged with black and the funeral held under much pomp and ceremony. The day after carried photographs of the procession. The elaborate hearse was draped in black silk, with the crown atop. The horses were dressed in black and gold with black ostrich feather headdresses. The mourners followed behind England at its best with the pomp and ceremony without comparison to the rest of the world.

The proclamation of Edward as King Edward VII, the Coronation planned for later that year. That state had moved from Victorians to Edwardians. The house still Saxe-Coburg-Gotha.

Two years later Jessica was once again pregnant, this time she was more tired than ever, she was thirty -seven years old and had three children already. Lillian had started school and Wilfred, who was rather slow and couldn't speak properly. No matter how Jessica tried with his pronunciation he still had trouble, she put it down to the fact that he had had a difficult birth and taking a rather long time to breathe had somehow impaired his progress. Matthew on the other hand, although a year and a half younger was adventurous and lively and seemed always to be the leader of the two boys.

When her time came Jessica sent Lillian next door to call Mrs. Upton who collected the children and took them to her house. She sent her eldest, Alice to call on Mrs. Smith and when she returned left Alice in charge of the children while she once again went in to sit with Jessica.

'You know Jess, he's going to kill you if you keep letting him have his way every time he drinks', she said gently.

Jessica, with sweat standing out on her brow nodded and gasped,

"Sooner it be me rather that the children being beaten, he uses his aggression this way.'

As Jessica pushed, Mrs. Smith, who had arrived a few minutes earlier cautioned her,

'Careful Jess, this little blighters feet first, we've got to be careful this time'.

After what seemed to Jessica an eternity, she pushed and very gently Mrs. Smith assisted a new baby girl into the world, no sooner had she cleaned the baby's airways that Jessica felt the urge to push once again and a baby boy was born, this time head first made his entrance. This was something no one was prepared for and Jessica was unsure whether to laugh or cry, four was bad enough in five years, but five!

The babies were called Florrie and Harry and once again the family of seven settled down, Jessica juggling with the problems of food and clothing.

Another year passed, Lillian was working well at school and Jessica was convinced that the halfpenny a week spent on her education was well worth it. She was now managing to knit a little more and her sewing was also improving. Wilfred had also started school, but was still very slow and his speech was not at all good.

Jessica was pregnant again, the twins were crawling and by now she had stopped worrying how she would cope, because she knew that she would somehow. The baby was born, another boy, they named him Charles, but quickly began calling him Charlie; it ran off the tongue easier.

CHAPTER 38

By 1906 Jessica was nearing her fortieth birthday, it was February and bitterly cold, Florrie, one of the twins went down with what they all thought was a cold the rest of the children had had colds and sniffles for the whole of the new year, so Jessica was not surprised by this after their initial fever they had all recovered. Florrie lay on the couch; she did not appear to be showing any signs of recovery she was listless, not wanting to interact with anyone or anything. Little Harry was by this time just learning to walk whilst Florrie was still not making an effort in this direction. Harry would half crawl, half walk to Florrie's side to try to get her to play, but to no avail.

Jessica became very worried, she had requested the doctor call, but he had to admit that he was unsure as to the cause of Florrie's illness. Florrie gradually became weaker. On Friday evening, Jessica gently bathed the weak child, dressed her and after numerous attempts to get her to eat eventually put her into bed beside Harry.

In the early hours of the morning Jessica heard Harry crying, she lit the candle and tiptoed over the cold floor. She walked over to the small bed where the two tiny forms lay together. As soon as she touched Florrie she knew she was no longer with them. Little Florrie was cold, she must have died earlier and her cold little body had awoken Harry.

Jessica gasped; she picked Harry up in her arms and rushed into the bedroom where George was still sleeping oblivious of the fact that his wife had left the bed. George awoke probably disturbed by Jessica gasping for breath, he turned over. As soon as he saw Jessica's face in the candlelight he could see something was wrong. She was standing shaking from head to foot, cradling little Harry while the tears poured down her face. George arose, dressed and left the house to collect the doctor. Jessica sat in frozen silence hugging the now sleeping child.

The next three days were a nightmare. Harry was unwell, the other children seemed also to be depressed, the tiny body was laid out in its little oak coffin in the front room where members of the family called to look at the little body and to offer their condolences.

Panic set in, as Harry over those days became just a listless as his sister had seemed earlier. Although Jessica could see that he was not well, his face white and drawn his eyes becoming sunken Jessica still clung to the hope that he was missing his sister desperately and was thus listless because of this.

The day of the funeral arrived, the coffin was sealed, a spray of laurel was placed on top and the family awaited the hearse. Mrs. Upton came in to look after the other children, she saw Harry had fallen asleep on the couch; she went over and lifted the child to put him in his bed the tiny frail body simply relaxed. Harry had followed his sister and had died peacefully in his sleep.

Mrs. Upton replaced the little body and went to the door to call George. She explained to George, whispering gently in his ear, with words that would scarcely form on her lips. George looked at her in total disbelief. As he put his arm around Jessica she new what had happened, she ran back inside the house shouting 'Oh God, Oh God'

It was after the funeral of her second twin that Jessica felt the stirrings of a new life inside her, this one she thought has been given, this one has been offered in exchange, but I would sooner not have been put through this torture in the first place. It first time in her life when she had doubted her belief in God.

The death of the twins seemed to have taken so much out of both George and Jessica's life that in the evenings when the children were asleep they sat in silence while Jessica intermittently rose and checked that all her children were breathing and never a night went by that Jessica did not rise from her bed to check again that nothing was wrong.

CHAPTER 39

Christmas 1907 was a sombre one, Jessica was still re-covering from the death of her babies and money was very short. She had, however, managed to buy all the children an orange and an apple and had a few nuts for Lillian and Wilfred. In addition she had salvaged the good pieces of material from one of her aprons and made Lillian one, she had crocheted some beautiful lace as a trim and embroidered dainty blue flowers on it.

It was Christmas Eve, Jessica had the pudding boiling away on the stove and George as yet, but predictably was nowhere to be seen. When he came home he had drunk his fill, not enough to be drunk, but enough to make him irrational.

'Time for bed children' Jessica announced as she lit the small candle to light them to bed. They all rose, knowing their father's temper on occasions such as these; they knew dallying was the last thing to do. On the way up stairs Lillian said, 'Mam, what am I getting for Christmas?'

Before Jessica could answer, George answered, 'Nowt, not know you've asked'.

Lillian cried herself to sleep; she awoke early hoping her father's threat was false this time. She went downstairs in the darkness, lit the lamp in the living room and saw a box with her name on it, she opened it and inside was everything needed to light the fire, matches, papers wood and small pieces of coal. Lillian was never to forget this Christmas. (Lillian was my grandmother and was indeed never to forget this; she related the story each time I asked for something as a child)

Later in the day when George was asleep, her mother called her into the scullery, she kissed her young daughter and said,

'Happy Christmas love, take these and take yourself a walk outside to eat them and never tell your Dad I disobeyed him'.

'Thanks Mam, I love you', said Lillian.

CHAPTER 40

The birth of William Collins occurred the day of the 4th April 1908; another healthy baby boy when Jessica had hoped secretly that she would produce twins to replace her lost loved ones. William was a bonny boy from the start and by the time he was six months old had a beautiful round ruddy face. He always seemed to be laughing,

'You love life don't you my darling?' Jessica said cuddling the bouncing baby, 'you're so happy'.

When William was two, once again Jessica was pregnant. 'How many more'? She asked George,

'I thought at forty-two I'd have been finished with this' George simply shrugged his shoulders and smiled.

'Well nobody can say we're not a good breeding pair, as the old Queen would have said, we're doing our bit for the country'.

It was whilst Jessica was collecting the last of the washing from the line she felt a strange heavy feeling in her stomach. She walked slowly to the privy where it happened, a sudden gush, a torrent of blood and she knew this baby was simply not to be. She felt strange, she thought she would be saddened at the loss, but somehow, deep inside she knew there had been something not quite as it should be and God forbid she produce a child who either would not survive or be damaged some way. She knew she would have coped, but with so many other children to look after this may simply have been too difficult to bear.

By 1910, the children were growing off hand nicely; Lillian was twelve and was able to take some of the chores from her mother. George, however, had begun drinking heavily and was becoming violent. One evening he returned home at about eight-thirty, but already reeling under the influence. Charlie and William were in bed and Jessica was reading the children's favourite story of David and Goliath to Lillian, Matthew and Wilfred, when George burst through the door.

'Get them kids out the way you', he exclaimed.

William ran, he was still too timid Matthew glared at his father, but knew better than to stand his ground. The two boys went upstairs; Lillian moved over to where her mother was sitting, she placed her arm around her mothers' shoulder.

'You Off', shouted George.

Lillian stood her ground.

'Off', he screamed through his drunken breath.

'No, I'll not move from Mam', Lillian had never dared address her father like this and was now looking and feeling terrified at her outward defiance.

'Go love, I'll be alright', whispered Jessica, terrified not only for herself, but also for her daughter.

Before Lillian could move however, George had crossed the room and had grabbed Jessica by the arm; he pulled her from her mother and threw her across the room. The force

154

was such that Lillian hit the wall with such a bang that her arm was badly jolted, Lillian went up to bed, tears welling up in her eyes, but determined not to cry. She lay in bed listening to her father shouting at her mother whilst her mother pleaded for no more abuse.

Lillian laid awake most of the night, her wrist searing with pain, the following morning her arm was swollen. Jessica took her daughter to visit the doctor, begging her not to reveal the true source of the injury. The doctor examined the wrist and discovered the break; he bound it and gave a very sceptical look when Lillian said she had fallen on an uneven path. (Again my grandmother related this story, all her life she suffered from arthritis in her wrist possibly as a result of this violent attack)

That year changed them once again; this time from Edwardians to Georgians as the King passed away and King George V was proclaimed king at his side was the tall, beautiful and elegant Mary of Tek.

There had been much merrymaking and Jessica had that year bought a very large Union Jack, which she was to balance on its pole on numerous occasions from the bedroom window, she was never alone in this action as the majority of people in Judges Street would do the same.

Lillian was by now fourteen years old Wilfred thirteen, Matthew was eleven. Lillian and Wilfred were working, whilst Matthew was still at school, much to his chagrin, as he just lived for the day when he could get away from home and only have to see his father infrequently. He loved his mother, but the idea of seeing George continue as before he found totally repulsive. Lillian was working on the floor at the local dye works and young Wilfred too slow to have much responsibility, swept the floor. However, he was still shrewd, and saved any moneey he had for his future.

'I can't be pregnant again wailed Jessica to Mrs. Upton, I'm forty-six, it's just the change'

'Well Jess, you are putting on weight, your face looks blooming, are you sure, and I think you're more or less certain you are, otherwise you wouldn't be wanting me to tell you otherwise'.

When Jessica felt the baby move, she knew she had been right all along.

In November 1910 Louise was born, she was a pretty baby, very dark skinned with black curly hair. Louise was not a happy baby, perhaps she sense her father's violence, and was wary of him.

A year later on 27th February 1911 George was born, again a bonny baby. Jessica was managing the house quite well now, as in addition to the money George senior brought in, there were earnings from Lillian, Wilfred and young Matthew was earning a little.

Lillian had met a young man at the dye works and although only fifteen years old was very attached to him. The young mans' name was Arthur, Arthur Vesty. He was twenty years old, a little too much of a difference for Jessica, especially at the tender age of fifteen. He was about five feet three inches tall, of slight build with the most beautiful blue eyes and fair hair just on the darker shade of blond. He was a very devoted churchgoer, church was his way of life, and nothing would keep him away from chapel on a Sunday. Arthur lived in a village called Quorn in School Street.

Around the time that Lillian met Arthur there were signs of unrest in Europe. Not long afterwards the archduke Ferdinand was assassinated in Sarajevo. The assassination of the Archduke and his wife was to be the catalyst of the world being plunged into war.

It seemed the only person enthusiastic about the war in the family was Matthew. He simply could not wait to join the army and fight. It seemed if he couldn't fight his father then he would need to channel his energy into fighting the Bosch at the earliest opportunity.

One morning Wilfred came downstairs as Jessica was lighting the fire.

'Where's Matt mother?' He asked.

'Upstairs with the rest of you', she said, as she brushed the range with black lead until it shone.

'E's not there Mother, I heard him get up while it was still dark, I thought he'd gone to the lavy, e didn't come back Mother, so I thought he was having trouble in sleeping and he'd stayed down here'.

Jessica sensed something was wrong; she pulled herself up from her knees and wiped her hands on her apron. She looked around as if looking for Matthew, noticed a piece of paper on the dresser that hadn't been there before. Jessica crossed the room dreading what she would find written on the paper. She once again wiped her hands on her apron as if trying to wipe away any anxiety and picked up the paper. It was written in Matthews's large clumsy hand and was simply addressed TO MOTHER. Jessica opened the folded paper slowly and carefully as if it would fall to pieces like a dried dead leaf if she mishandled it. It read: -

MAM
I'VE GONE TO FIGHT FOR US\WE'L BEAT THE BOSCH
LOOK AFTER YOURSELF AND THE KIDS
I LOVE YOU
MATTHEW

Jessica sat in her chair by the fire, the paper flapping in her hands, she hadn't lit the fire, all she could say was 'Matt oh Matt'.

Wilfred moved over to her and said

'Don't worry Mam, he'll be alright, he could always look after himself'.

Jessica buried her head in her hands and sobbed. Wilfred lit the fire, filled the kettle and placed it on the hob. He walked over to the cupboard, took out the pots and the bread and set the table, just as his mother had done ever since he could remember.

When George came down his head was aching from the over indulgence of the previous evening, he raged when told of Matthews' leaving, still in a rage he announced he would call in at the Police Station and report Matthew missing and also instruct them, when they found him, to beat him with the birch, keep him overnight to teach him a lesson.

Jessica begged George not to tell the Police that, saying all she wanted was he son back that was quite enough. She knew that if George had told the police that, then they would carry out his instructions to the letter and she considered her son had put up with enough problems already, otherwise why would he have needed to get away at all? George said, he wasn't bothered what she wanted and stormed out of the house, slamming the door behind him.

Matthew sat on the train listening to the other young men around him talking animatedly about the fighting with great excitement. He had managed to convince the recruitment officer that he was seventeen years old whilst in truth he was not quite fifteen. He had been given a uniform with boots that were too big, but had been reminded that he was still young and would grow into them.

Matthew gazed out of the train window, he had never travelled away from home before and had certainly never envisaged travelling on a train, now the countryside was dashing past at an alarming rate providing little opportunity to focus on the land close to the train. He decided to focus on the landscape in the distance, which to his eyes appeared to remain in focus far longer.

Matthew was travelling to where a training camp had been established. When he arrived in a camp near Maidstone, where once again Matthew had his next real experience in that he saw the sea for the first time. The training was hard, he was taught to shoot his rifle he was taught how to fix a bayonet and the theory of close contact fighting. It was at this time he began to fear for his life. To shoot at a target that could just be seen or in some circumstances not be seen at all, to learn to fire the cannon again produced little concern to his young mind, but to actually kill someone close up, just because they were wearing a different uniform and believed in different ideologies was totally alien. It was too late now, he was in the army, he couldn't admit to his tender age for fear of being arrested and besides that all around him were young men not much older that himself, they were brave enough to have enlisted.

Matthew travelled to Dover where he was given his orders. He waited alongside the hundreds of others to board a ship on the first phase of a journey to Turkistan. It was here that he was intercepted and taken to the local police station where he admitted he had lied about his age.

Jessica slept very little over the next two weeks, her precious Matthew was missing and he above all her sons understood her problems and had helped her through them on innumerable occasions.

Two weeks after Matthew had left, Jessica was preparing

the dinner when there was a knock at the door. She went to answer it and as she opened it she could see it was a Police Constable, Jessica gasped.

'Good afternoon Mrs. Collins, it is Mrs. Collins isn't it?' he enquired.

'That's right'. Said Jessica cautiously.

'You've got a son called', he reached into his pocket for his note book and opened it, 'Matthews, yes, that's it, Matthew'.

Jessica simply nodded, her heart pounding, the colour slowly draining from her face.

He's on his way back missus, he's been on quite and adventure', his smile faded, he'll be brought back tomorrow, but as your husband insisted on us birching him before his return he won't come to your house until the day after'.

Jessica rested on the doorjamb; the policeman moved forward and caught hold of her arm,

'Alright missus, come on I'll help you to your seat', he helped her into the living room and to her chair. Jessica's head was swimming, she felt sick and afraid for her son.

I'll be off now love, don't worry he's a strong lad, he'll smart for a few days, but I'm sure he'll soon be back to his old self', he slowly walked towards the door.

'See you take care missus, take care.' With that he gently closed the door behind him, leaving Jessica alone with the younger children.

Jessica spent most of the night lay turning over and over, falling asleep only when she was completely exhausted. When she awoke the next morning her hair was tinted with white, and gradually over the next year turned completely white. (Matthew through the rest of his life blamed himself for his Mother's hair turning white so quickly.)

Matthew returned home as scheduled, walking slowly because of the injuries he had received at the hands of the police.

CHAPTER 41

When Matthew had recovered from his injuries he was sitting beside his Mother and Lillian one evening when George was at the pub and the other children were in bed when he said: -

'Oh Mam, I've seen such things, I've got to go again some day, I can't stay here forever', he held Jessica's hand and Lillian moved closer towards them both.

'I know son, I know I'll never have you for my own again, you tasted a different world, one I know nothing about, tell me son, tell me what you've seen'. Jessica squeezed his hand tightly and smiled at him.

Matthew began by telling Jessica of the day he had been to enlist, he had told the Sergeant at the recruiting station he was seventeen and an orphan, he had taken the Kings Shilling and had immediately been given a rail ticket to the army camp. He had been taught the rudiments of infantry. He told his mother of the sights he had seen, about the size of London where he had crossed that capital city in order to change trains, he described the sea and sand, ships and sea gulls, sights and smells, whilst Jessica and Lillian sat spell bound.

War was declared officially that year and Jessica thanked the Lord her son had not succeeded in his adventure. After all by the time Matthew was really old enough to join the army there would be everlasting peace, this was going to be 'the war to end all wars' all the politicians said so. Her precious son would be safe forever.

In 1915, Arthur asked Lillian to marry him. Arthur had explained to Lillian that he thought it would be a good idea. The war in Europe had been raging for almost a year and Arthur felt duty bound to join the ranks. Lillian ran home breathless to tell her mother.

'Mam', she said, 'Arthur would like to come and talk to Dad'.

Jessica look troubled, she knew Arthur was very active in the temperance league and was concerned that if he saw her husband under the influence of drink, he might consider Lillian less than favourably for a wife and she knew how Lillian loved this man.

Lillian, in effect asked her father, George, surprisingly was in a good mood, he had recently changed his job and was enjoying life working in the factory at the end of the street, they had begun making armaments and cranes for the war effort.

'Alright gel', he said in an acquiescent manner.

'Tell him to come round tomorrow night after work, your mam'll get him a bite to eat and we'll talk before your Mam fetches mi beer from the beer off, I just hope he's not high an mighty about his religion and not drinking. I don't want a son-in-law who lectures'.

Lillian breathed a sigh of relief her only worry was what might Arthur say to her father.

Arthur made his request and was given permission to wed

Lillian. They were married in the spring of 1915. Aunt Mary, a family friend prepared some food and Lillian and her mother made the dress, decorated with fine embroidery.

Soon after they were married, Arthur was given his marching orders and Lillian returned to live with her mother.

CHAPTER 42

By October Lillian realised she was pregnant, she wrote to Arthur giving him the news, it arrived one day whilst Arthur was resting in one of the trenches. It was raining and Arthur had been sent from the front line to a safer trench for a rest, he was exhausted, he was cold and wet his head ached from the constant gunfire and he hadn't slept for days.

Arthur opened the letter, he recognised Lillian's handwriting and began to read with a smile, thank God he thought, thank God she doesn't even know where Belgium is, never mind the hell we're all suffering here.

Once Arthur was feeling refreshed, he, along with the others in his company were once again sent to the front lines. It was said that anyone who survived entering the front twice would be OK. As the company's of men from the Yorkshire Regiment made their way they passed the carts, dozens of them, all loaded with the dead, dying and injured, another offensive had begun and the casualties were heavier than they had ever been.

Arthur took out his letter from Lillian and held it tightly

in his hand as if he was holding her hand. He tucked it safely inside his Bible that he put in his inside pocket over his heart. Arthur could hear the shells and the gunfire, he could smell the cordite and hear the groans of the injured men being transported to the field hospitals, where they knew although the doctors and medics would give them the best possible treatment, some would not survive and others would only go home to spend the rest of their lives in wheelchairs.

Arthur trudged through the mud, it seemed as though it had been raining in this God forsaken country since the beginning of time, his feet were wet, his boots were heavy, his waterproof was heavy with water and tears from the wood and nails in the trenches had left spaces for the water to enter and soak him to the skin.

The slowly moving column of men was barely discernable; they had merged into the muddy countryside, a gigantic muddy worm, wriggling slowly across the bomb-cratered land.

As they neared the front line a shell landed and screams could be heard, a horse and cart went by, the horse panicked by the shell, the cart on its side being dragged along, its' driver entangled in the traces screaming. Two men made an attempt to stop the horse, but to no avail, eventually one of the soldiers shot the terrified animal, it fell, it was too late to save the driver, his body had been cut to an unrecognisable shape by the cart with which he had become entrapped.

George passed the bodies of more horses, their bodies bloated with the gases, their legs sticking out stiff like some strange animated balloon, they were in the later stages of rigor mortis.

Arthur became even more nervous as he made a private prayer requesting he be spared long enough to see his first child and to be able to return home to normalisation away from this alien place where he could ill imagine any human being wishing to inhabit.

The column fed into the trench, the mud seemed even more stained than when Arthur had last seen it, the men even more red eyed and weary.

A shell exploded just short of its goal, showering the men below with wet clods of earth. More shells followed, another barrage was underway, the British forces had not advanced an inch for more than three weeks, and it had simply sat, being continually under fire supplying more fodder, as its defences were bloody and beaten.

Arthur and his allies moved up, they tapped their compatriots on the shoulder, and relieved them of their positions.

Arthur's best friend Tom Packe, who had been with Arthur from enlistment to the present time and who also came from the same village tapped the shoulder of the man next to Arthur, he didn't move, he placed a hand on his shoulder, and said,

'Come on mate, give it a rest'

The man slid slowly down from his position into a rigid mass on the duckboards which made up the base of the trench, he had been shot in the head, and who knew how long previously he had died at his post. One of the team of men detailed to clear the dead and injured from the trench quickly moved forward and the dead soldier was unceremoniously dragged from beneath the feet of the living.

Tom Packe cursed and said to Arthur,

'You know Arthur, I don't think we'll make it this time'.

Arthur replied that he desperately needed to, because he wanted to see his as yet unborn child.

The Bosch were moving forward, so close now that for the

first time in an age they were on both sides able to use their rifles to greater effect. Arthur was just returning from a visit to the latrines and a drink of hot sweet black tea, when he felt a searing pain in his shoulder, he thought it was simply cramp in his muscle due to having kept in one position for too long. It was only when his blood trickled down his arm and clogging his fingers that he realised he had been hit. What Arthur couldn't understand was that it didn't hurt, although his fingers were becoming numb. I've been hit he shouted to Tom above the noise of another volley.

'Well get the hell.....................' this was the last words Tom Packe spoke, a shell landed immediately in front of him as he turned to speak to Arthur and all Arthur could remember seeing, before he was violently sick was Tom's helmet landing at his feet.

Arthur woke up in the field hospital, his shoulder ached, and he was having trouble focusing. He could hear a man gabbling and crying hysterically.

'My legs, Oh God, why didn't you do a complete job, I can't live like this'. Arthur heard the light quick step of a nurse and a soft voice, followed by the cry of a man subsiding into low whimpering like a puppy crying for its mother on the first night away.

As his vision cleared, he could see men with sunken eyes wandering around, minds on some other plain, no longer able to say who they were, or even knowing what they had become.

He saw limbless men laying shocked into silence, men thrown into a lifetime of darkness, or silence. A nurse came to the side of his bed, 'Private Vesty'?

'Yes Nurse', Arthur said softly.

'You're lucky, that bullet went straight through, just tore a

167

bit of muscle, and you'll soon be as good as new'.

"No nurse, no man's lucky if he's been to hell', he said.

The doctor visited the day after,

'We need that bed Private, it's home for you until you're mended, give em what for when you return eh'?

Arthur could only nod.

CHAPTER 43

Within the week Arthur was on the boat making his way home, his arm was in a sling and except for this there was no more outward sign of him having been at the front.

The journey home through the English countryside held no allure for him as he stared blankly out of the train window. Even the prospect of seeing his family once again seemed remote.

He alighted from the train and began to walk the short distance home it was the beginning of May, the streets were dotted with children playing with hoops, marbles and whip and tops. He smiled as a little girl rushed past having hit her hoop with more force than intended; the hoop was careering down the hill with the child in hot pursuit.

The sight of the small child appeared as in slow motion, her clattering shoes as a mere drum beat in an empty space. Even the small pleasures of children playing appeared muffled in the semi dream like state experienced by Arthur.

Arthur turned the corner, and walked up the street to

number 33 Judges Street, he knocked at the front door, even this was unusual as no one other than the doctor or important visitors ever knocked on the front door, the back was the normal entry route.

He listened to the person inside walk through the parlour, the bolt withdrawn, the key being turned and the creaking of the seldom-used front door being opened.

At the door stood Lillian, stout and in the eighth month of her pregnancy, she looked at Arthur in total disbelief not knowing whether to laugh with joy at seeing him, or to cry with sorrow at the sight of his injury. Instead she threw her arms around him, it was only when he recoiled in pain did she realise she had indeed been a little over enthusiastic.

'It's OK Lillian, I'm not badly injured, not enough to keep me away forever, just enough to enable me to see our baby.'

He put his arms around Lillian's shoulder and led her inside, her head resting on his uninjured shoulder as he guided her into the living room.

Jessica was in the scullery pealing the potatoes when she heard Lillian talking; she dried her hands and entered the living room. She gasped, smiled broadly and rushed over to Arthur where she kissed him on the cheek, before saying,

'I'd better peel a few more and nip to the butchers for a bit more beef'

The boys treated Arthur like an unsung hero; Matthew especially wanted to know just what it was like, but Arthur, the shock of his experiences just beginning to have an impact on his mind could only answer.

'It's like nothing anyone has every experienced before, I'm just happy this will never happen again, men should never kill a fellow in anger, I'm just glad I've never fired my rifle.'

George Snr could see that Arthur's sufferings were beyond

description, he'd seen men killed, not in the way Arthur had, who, if newspaper accounts were to be believed were in their hundreds, but their torment afterwards lasted for years, who knew what Arthur would have to go through.

'Bed you lot' George said, 'the lads had enough now, and no more questions tomorrow either'.

They went without further word, 'an you two as well, we've all had enough excitement for one day, we'll need the energy for the next event soon enough'.

That night Arthur dreamed he was once again in the trenches, the shells were falling about him and he was trapped in the centre with his tiny child in his arms, his screams woke the whole of the household, his young wife was terrified, Lillian shook Arthur awake and he lay, sweat dripping from his body, his, shoulder aching.

'I'm sorry Lill', he said I had a bad dream, try to go to sleep, I'll be all right in a few minutes'.

Arthur lay awake for almost the rest of the hours of darkness and when he did eventually fall asleep he was restless and muttering in his sleep.

By the morning he had forgotten his dream and it wasn't until William, then nine years old mentioned the noise in the night that he remembered waking.

When George came home, Arthur went into the scullery, whilst George washed after his return from work, Arthur apologised, but George said he understood a little of what the young man had experienced, and that he was not to worry over it as it was a way his system had of dealing with worries.

By the time the baby was due to be born Arthur was physically recovering well. On the evening of the 29th June, Lillian began to experience the first of her labour pains. She was taken into the front room where the young couple slept. The rest of the family occupied the other rooms of the house. Arthur sat in Jessica's chair by the fire listening to the exclamations of pain from his young wife.

During the early hours of June 30th 1916 little Lillian Florence Vesty made her appearance. Lillian her mother was just eighteen years old and her husband twenty-three.

Arthur entered the room and sat on the bed where his wife sat cradling their tiny daughter. He kissed his wife and she passed him the child, as he held her he let her tiny fingers rest on his forefinger and sat in silence marvelling at the tiny perfect creature he had helped to make.

'I want her to grow up having both of us and I know that shortly I have to return Lil, I know they'll soon be sending for me'. He pulled the child closer to his body.

'Perhaps the war will be over before you're needed again' said Lillian, but they both secretly knew this was not possible.

The months that followed were precious to them both, they walked together in the park, over the fields and by the river, taking their baby everywhere with them.

By November the thing they had dreaded happened, Arthur received a letter ordering him to return to his unit. By then the Government had taken drastic measures at home, the army was short of shells and the coal mines and railways had taken over, The Government had also passed an act to take over factories in order to produce more of the needs of the forces. There was a shortage of men to work in the factories, drive the trams and therefore women for the first time went to work to do the jobs of their men who were fighting.

Arthur was once more sent overseas and Lillian left her baby in the care of her mother whilst she herself worked in the local engineering factory, which was now making munitions.

Arthur's return to the front was a traumatic time, he was mentally ill prepared for another time away, he missed his young wife and child and was still experiencing bouts of depression after the terrible experiences, especially after the death of his friend Tom Packe.

It was 1917, Arthur had seen and felt horrors that no human should experience. He had seen acquaintances shot by his own side they had lost their nerve, they had become insane, but instead of being treated in a sympathetic manner they were accused of cowardice and many met their ends at the end of their compatriots rifles.

Arthur knew, that if he was to meet his end he wanted it to be swift and hoped that it would no way be like some of his colleagues who lingered for many days and weeks in great pain before succumbing to the inevitable.

He received several letters from Lillian, all of which appeared to be lively and witty, he went on several rest releases into local towns where he made a point of buying beautifully embroidered postcards that he sent with short notes to Lillian. She placed these on the mantelpiece in their front room bedroom, she would take a last look at them and wish them goodnight as if their presence would carry the message to Arthur, and she then blew out the candle.

By Christmas 1917 Lillian had been to the local photographer who had taken a photograph of Lillian now aged eighteen months old, a child with dark curling hair and beautiful blue, grey questioning eyes. She posted this to Arthur with love and kisses for Christmas.

One day Jessica as was her usual habit walked to the corner shop, she had her basket over her arm and was just passing the time of day with Fanny Mee who lived next door to the shop.

'I'll be glad Jess when this lots done, I don't know why our lads av to go out there an fight, but I must say I suppose I'm glad they're keeping it over there not here'.

Fanny had a son Jim, fighting in Turkey and she was worried as she hadn't heard any news of him for some time.

'I know what you mean Fanny', said Jessica, 'I'd best be going now though else I'll never be done today, see you soon Fanny'.

Jessica turned to walk up the street, just as Jane Moore stopped to speak to Fanny, 'OK Jess'? Jane Asked

'Fine thank you Jane', Jessica answered.

Jessica walked up the street and was just opening the back gate when there was an enormous bang. Jessica held on to the entry wall and heard the clatter of crockery as the cups were catapulted from the kitchen shelf.

A German bomb had fallen, Fanny and Jane were killed instantly and rows of houses, including the shop were badly damaged.

CHAPTER 44

During 1917, Matthew once again made an attempt to enter the Army, by now the losses were catastrophic, younger lads were being accepted alongside men who had been considered too old for combat duty were also being accepted for 'cannon fodder'. Matthew had at last achieved his goal, this time returning home in his uniform, clothes wrapped in brown paper, complete with kit bag, puttees firmly in place, looking for all the world like a child ready for a fancy dress party, instead of a boy/man about to get his first taste of death and violence.

Jessica, tears welling up in her eyes gently kissed him, and accepted that her son was about to enter what to his romantic youth was an adventure of a lifetime. Jessica was terrified, already two young men from their street had been killed and another sent home to face life as a cripple, injured both mentally and physically, he had returned home to live the life of a child, he played with dolls, gabbled gibberish and wet himself. He had left a healthy happy young man; he had returned a useless little boy.

Matthew had his orders, he was to catch the train to a camp in Doncaster and from there he would travel to the East coast where he would board a ship to Belgium. He was full of excitement, he once again underwent initial training and boarded the boat that would take him across the sea, and he never got that far before.

The journey across the channel was rough and uncomfortable, they slept on the cold floor of the steamer, their heads resting on their packs, many of them were sick and by the time they landed, some faces already tired and drawn merely by the journey. They rested on the beaches where the local women with baskets on their arms walked amongst them distributing bread and sausage. Matthew still eager for his battle walked up and down the ranks speaking to the others asking some of the old men amongst them if they had ever been in a battle before and if so what it was like.

The next day they set off, refreshed after a nights rest, marching in step, and a healthy column of men going as if on a Sunday school outing. After a few hours marching the noise of the shells and gunfire grew louder, the big guns rumbled as if a gigantic thunder storm was raging overhead. They were now passing columns of men, these men were dragging themselves along, one called to the young men as they passed heading in the opposite direction.

'Don't be too eager to get there you'll have no youth left once you do'.

They did not see who uttered these words, but simply carried on walking.

The allies were making advances in the battle and the gunfire, although loud to their ears was actually moderating as the push to the German boarder was underway.

Matthew was unaware where Arthur was fighting, but assumed he was on the same front. The earth was interlaced with trenches, with street and town names of places they know from home, to help the men focus on what they were fighting for.

Matthew cut his fighting teeth early on, when his column was ordered to hit the ground as a shell travelled noisily overhead, earth flying in clods around them. The sounds of screams could be heard even above the volley that followed. Matthew was afraid for probably the first time in his life. He saw things that day which he would never discuss; he saw life snuffed out so quickly, not only life, but also human beings virtually disappearing as they were cut to ribbons in the blast.

Arthur was nearing the great city of Reims, now very close to the German border. He had walked for days and as with the rest of his division was exhausted. He knew that after a maximum of two days rest he would be required once more to join many others in an attempt to further weaken the defences of the German Army. Arthur clung to his letter from Lillian and the little photograph of his very tiny daughter. He patted his small Bible his salvation in these troubled times.

The fighting had now reached the town of Soissons, the houses wrecked, the magnificent church riddled with bullet holes, marring the proud dressed stone. Just outside the town

Muddied, smelly creatures, all proud men who had fought for what seemed a lifetime, inhabited the trenches. Arthur felt the fear of death in his heart as he took up his position in the front trench. As the whistle blew to signal yet another flight to the dry land outside the trench, Arthur went over the top alongside other brave and innocent men who still wondered how they came to be in this God forsaken situation. The German barrage began, the men ran, guns sticking out in front as a host of water diviners, heads down, hearts pounding. As the advance moved forward men on all sides fell, some mortally wounded, some having suffered a quick seemingly painless death, killed so quickly that they had no time to shout or moan, but simply sank into the earth breathing the last of their breaths. Arthur was one of these casualties, dying on the 23rd June 1918. At the end of this tragic war he was buried in the tiny military cemetery of Jonchery–sur-Vesle. So close to the end of the war, so near to being able to see his family, but life did not deal him the survival card.

CHAPTER 45

Jessica had placed the baby in her cot for a sleep, when there was a knock at the front door. She hurried to answer it before another knock awoke Lillian Florence. Jessica stood and stared at the young policeman, he removed his helmet, 'Mrs. Vesty'.

Jessica breathed a sigh of relief, she had thought it was about Matthew, but her relief was to be short lived.

'She's at work, what is it?"

'It's bad news I'm afraid Missis', he answered.

'How bad?' asked Jessica.

'As bad as it can be I'm afraid, it is Mrs. Vesty what's married to Arthur Vesty isn't it?' he enquired.

'That's right, Oh God, how do you tell your daughter it's her husband that's been killed, and her little baby is fatherless'? She fumbled with her words.

'Can you do it by yourself missus?' the young policeman enquired.

'Don't worry lad, I dare say you've had your fill of telling disasters', Jessica said.

'Five today missus, five and more coming in all the time, it's looking real bad, if you don't need me no more I'll go now'.

'Yes, yes, ' said Jessica, 'I'll manage somehow'

She closed the door and leant on its cold surface, she sat on her daughter's bed and gently touched the quilt.

'God, what did we all do to deserve such heartbreak, we never had it this way in my younger days, why do the young today have to suffer so'? She buried her head in her hands and wept.

When she had composed herself, Jessica knocked on the wall to alert Mrs. Upton, who was quick to respond, Jessica explained what had happened and Mrs. Upton said she would watch the children whilst Jessica went the mile to the factory where Lillian was working to give her daughter the news.

Jessica walked slowly to the factory, going over and over in her mind how she could tell her child. As it was she had no need for words. Jessica called at the office and asked to speak to Lillian, the young secretary went away and returned with Lillian, as Lillian entered the room she looked at her mother, immediately her forefinger, with hand clenched was thrust into her mouth to stifle a scream, and she bit down hard. Jessica moved forward, nodded gently, placed her arm around her daughter's shoulder and guided her to a chair.

The company was very good and an automobile was called, which took both Jessica and Lillian back home. The neighbours stood at their doorways as they saw the car draw up at number 33. When they saw the two distraught women alight, they didn't need any further information.

A death without a funeral takes longer to recover from and the effect on Lillian was no different in this respect than any other woman.

Matthew was notified by letter from his mother, the fighting had worsened, but he had been lucky, when he heard of Arthur's death he was so fired with anger, that from then on if a German soldier had crossed his path during that bloody war, he would not have crossed back.

Lillian received a citation signed by the King, two medals and a bronze disc depicting Britannia and a Lion with the inscription, 'He died for Freedom and Honour', Arthur Vesty, Lillian had them set in a carved frame, with yet another inscription 'Lest we forget', carved into it.

CHAPTER 46

Nineteen eighteen and Armistice Day arrived, the flag which Jessica had purchased for the coronation in happier times was flown, everyone celebrated. In the Collins household there was a mixture of happiness and sorrow, as with many households up and down the country, life would never be the same again.

The war over, Jessica thought this may return to the old ways, in her life she had seen so many changes, the world appeared to have become a noisy place where the birds had to compete for a space to sing and a space to fly.

Monday morning came, Jessica had finished her washing and had pegged it on the line; it was a warm June day in 1919. Jessica was used to having a conversation over the fence with Jane Upton, but this morning Jane hadn't been seen. Jessica opened the gate and went to Jane's door; she knocked gently, at the same time calling softly, ' Jane, are you there is everything alright?'

Jane came to the door and opened it; she was just two years older than Jessica, although she had had her children earlier.

When Jessica looked at Jane she couldn't help exclaiming loudly, 'god, Jane what's up?'

Jane led Jessica inside the house and once more flopped down on the large fireside chair where she had been resting, her face was ashen and drawn, she seemed so thin, yet Jessica hadn't noticed this before, losing weight a little yes, but Jessica put this down to the change.

'Jess', said Jane, 'I think I'm really ill, I've got a lump on my breast and one under my arm, they've been growing for some time, but now they're bursting and I can't eat. I feel sick all the time and I'm in such pain.

'Let's look', said Jessica matter of factly.

Jane showed her the large cancerous eruptions, she had heard tales about this sort of thing, but had never seen anything like the terrible open sores that Jane now exposed.

Jessica sat down in the chair opposite and reached out with both hands, clasping Jane's bony hands, she just looked at Jane, no words were needed, and they both knew the outcome of this disease well enough.

Jane Upton became weaker over the next few weeks and Jessica spent every spare minute of the day sitting with Jane. Initially she had taken on the washing and ironing, a little later she began cooking. Jane's husband provided a little extra money from his wages and subsidised this by vegetables from his garden plot. Jane managed, to begin with, to do a little housework, but as time went by, she spent longer and longer in bed. Jessica was with her at the end, she had taken shifts to sit with Sam Upton and on this particular evening Sam had fallen asleep in the chair, Jessica was holding Jane's hand as she slept for the first time in days, suddenly Jane squeezed Jessica's hand, called out in a loud voice, 'Sam' and lay back on the pillow.

Sam awoke immediately and came to his wife's side, he looked at his wife, then at Jessica, she shook her head and got up, Jessica went outside leaving Sam to grieve by Jane's side.

After the doctor had gone Sam called on Jessica, Jessica had laid a few people out in her time and he now asked her to do him the favour of laying out her best friend. Jessica asked Lillian to help and between them they washed their friend giving her a last goodbye.

After the funeral was over Jessica said,

'I can't lay out ever again Lill, but I think you could carry on and of course it's a little bit extra'.

CHAPTER 47

L illian had been seeing a man called George Trueman; he had worked with both her and Arthur before the war and had been a good friend.

George had served in the army during the war and had been in the army before the war serving in India. In India he had contracted Malaria and unfortunately was, on occasions, laid low with Malarial Fever, which would be with him for the rest of his life. George was a strong man of medium height; with an impressive physique he had been a champion fisticuffs fighter in the army. George's body was an impressive array of tattoos, a sailing ship on his chest, a signet ring on his finger, the statutory heart with a sash saying 'Mother', even a female whose body was tightly woven by a snake, when his wriggled his fingers the body wriggled.

Lillian and George married in April 1920 and moved into a small house next to the factory where he worked. They left little Lillian Florence in the capable hands of Jessica and set about making a home for themselves.

Lillian became pregnant once again and in 1921 gave birth

to another daughter whom she called Louise Margaret. Lillian was not too happy living away from her mother and young daughter, especially as she couldn't visit her every day.

When the baby was two months old Lillian had placed her in the corner of the room in her pram, where she soon settled down to her morning sleep. The local farmer drove his cattle down the street every morning; the farm was split after the building of the factory and that necessitated him driving his cattle to the milking parlour. On this occasion some thing spooked one of the cows that deviated from the road and somehow entered the open door of Lillian's parlour.

The cow panicked as it could not get out, Lillian was panic stricken as she couldn't get to her baby, hearing the commotion the baby had awoken and was screaming, the farmer and a neighbour risked great injury whilst trying to release the cow, eventually they managed this with no damage to Louise.

Lillian was forever afraid of cows after that episode. At this time, Sam Upton decided to move house to a tiny cottage close to his daughter; therefore number 31 Judges Street became vacant. When the rent man arrived for his weekly rent from Jessica she broached the subject. It was readily agreed that Lillian and George could move into the house.

Lillian set about packing her home whilst George began to decorate their new home. There was little furniture to move as most of the living room furniture had been smashed. Mr. Briggs, the farmer called at their new home, he offered George Trueman some work after his day at the factory was concluded, plus he gave them some money to aid in the replacement of their furniture. Mr. Briggs and George became firm friends for the rest of their lives.

CHAPTER 48

A year later Wilf came home and announced he was thinking of getting married. 'Good God', said George Collins, 'I didn't think you had the kokum lad, when are we going to see this woman then?'

'When she's in town again Dad', said Wilf smiling.

'What's she do then?' Jessica said quite interested in her son's bride to be, and her future daughter –in-law.

'She er travels mam', Wilfred said cagily, 'she travels'.

'Where did you meet her then?' George asked.

'Down the lane', Wilf said once again smiling.

'Funny place to meet and romance for the first time, just what was she doing down the lane?' Jessica put in again.

'Her name's Mary, Mam and she was living there', Wilfred said, now a little edgy.

'There's no houses down the lane', said George curious about his son's answers.

'Nobody but Gypsies live down the lane son', said Jessica, assuming her son had once again become confused.

'She's not one of them is she son?' George asked not too

sure about Jessica's thoughts.

'Yes Mam, yes Dad, she's a traveller, they don't call themselves Gypsies, an Mam she's the pretty one with the lovely black wavy hair and brown eyes who sold you the wooden chrysanthemums last month.'

'They've all got bloody black wavy hair son, as they're still bloody Gypsies, how do you think that sort would ever settle, they ain't ever even had a bath', George slammed his fist on the table.

'Get the bloody idea out of your head son', George said as he sat down again.

'Why do my children always fare wrong?' Jessica threw her arms in the air and slumped in the chair.

Wilfred carried on his romance with Mary and eventually Jessica said, 'You'd better bring her to tea on Sunday'.

'Yes Mam,' said Wilfred, 'Mam, we need to get married soon though, or she'll be a bit big'.

Jessica said in her mind, you bloody fool son, but to her son, she said, 'Just as well I kept Flo's things, Lillian Florence had now become plain and simple Flo. Jessica then turned and carried on with her chores.

The following Sunday, Wilfred went to meet Mary, he returned alone.

'Where is she then?' said George.

'She's at the bottom of the entry, she's never been in a house before an she's a bit worried Mam', said Wilfred looking worried.

'She's got to make the journey, unless you're going to live under a hedge', said George irritably, 'and anyway go off and make her move, I'm ready for my tea'.

Wilfred went out and soon returned with Mary, she was young, not more than sixteen or seventeen, dark, swarthy skinned and small, she and Wilfred seemed like a pair of bookends, they were so close in size.

Mary sat perched on the edge of the chair and when Jessica placed one of her china cups and saucers in front of her she looked at Wilfred, not daring to drink, he whispered, '

'Just watch Mam and copy what she does'. This accomplished, together with holding the plate and eating neatly, the conversation began.

George reached for his large bowled briar pipe with tobacco taken from a tin obviously much used,

'Tell us about yourself',

He lit a match and took several long puffs on the pipe until the contents of the bowl glowed.

'Come on, you can't be shy if you're to enter this family; it's too big to have secrets'.

'Ain't nuthin to tell, me names Mary Atkins, that's all', said Mary used a strange Romany type accent, a mixture of all the regional accents she was used to visiting rolled into one.

'How old are you gel?' said Jessica.

'Don't know, but I suppose around seventeen or there about', said Mary.

'An if you're to marry Wilf, where do you propose to live'? Butted in George.

'Not thought about it', said Mary, now growing a little uneasy with the questions.

'Well, I suggest you two start looking for a house to rent this afternoon, as by the looks of you girl, you'll not have time taken to make the bed before the baby's born'. Jessica said matter of factly.

'How longs she got Mam', asked Wilfred.

'That's what she should know son.'

'Can't you reckon girl?'

'No, Mrs. Collins, never learnt how', said Mary, wriggling about on her chair.

'Heaven preserve us', said Jessica to the ceiling, 'On your way both of you, look for a place and visit the Minister to set a date', Jessica pointed to the door.

The young couple rose and once outside Mary stopped and looked into Wilfred's eyes,

'How will we manage?'

'I don't know if I can live in a cage like that'.

'You'll get used to it, you'll have to duck', said Wilfred.

They walked down the street, Jessica was correct; as Mary gripped Wilfred's hand she had certainly developed the kind of waddle usually developed in the later stages of pregnancy.

They managed to find a house in the afternoon, which seemed to be the least of their troubles. When it came to a Minister, it was different.

Mary said her family never went to Church and had never had the need of a Minister. Wilfred said he would never be allowed to be married to her if they didn't use a Minister and due to the fact that Jessica had voiced her concern about the amount of time left before her confinement they didn't have time to argue, or the baby would be left without a name.

Eventually, they came to an agreement, they were married in Chapel and Wilfred's family attended, and after that they were 'joined' by jumping the broom at a ceremony held by Mary's family.

The niceties out of the way, Mary and Wilf could begin to set up home. Each day Wilfred arrived home he would find Mary crocheting beautiful coloured baby clothes, whilst sitting on a chair in the back yard, she only ate and slept indoors and for the most part could be found outside when Wilfred was at work.

The baby arrived two months after the wedding, they called her Rose, she was a tiny thing resembling her mother, but with her father's small nose and sparkling eyes. Whenever Mary's folks were in town she would leave the home and return to stay with them, Wilfred always returned home to his mother on these occasions.

CHAPTER 49

It was by now 1923, even little George was now ten years old, and the family was better off and by now a more manageable size. With Lillian and Wilfred married with families of their own and Matthew still pursuing his career as a soldier. The world around them seemed to be changing dramatically even young women were seen walking into town alone in the evenings, a thing unheard of in Jessica's youth. The skirts of the young girls were becoming shorter and brighter and some now wore lipstick and powder, a habit George Collins definitely disapproved of.

'You'd never av seen this in my time', he said on several occasions.

By the time Lillian Florence was fourteen years old she was wanting make –up, stockings etc., of course George would not allow this, and the only way she could have the same as the other girls was to call on Lillian next door, both before and after going out, where she would re-do her hair and put lipstick on.

Charlie had been walking a young lady called Emily out

for sometime. He was working for a local coal haulage company whose office was in a nearby village and had met Emily as she had worked in the office. Jessica often joked at the thought of Charlie standing in the office waiting for his pay, covered from head to foot in coal dust, eyes shining like lanterns and teeth looking for all the world like the false sets in the dentists, as they reflected against his dirty face. On several occasions when Emily had been to tea, Jessica said,

'How come you could tell what was under that muck gel? I'm sure I don't recognise him myself when e's in his muck'

Emily, was a relaxed happy girl and would reply jokingly,

'Me Mam always said look for the muck an you'll find the money Mrs. Collins'.

Then they would both chuckle loudly at the thought of every being rich.

When Charlie and Emily married, it was the prettiest wedding Jessica had seen, Emily was an only child and her parents had worked hard to give their daughter a really good wedding. Even Jessica could afford a new hat, dress and coat. Charlie and Emily moved into the village where he worked, they were very happy.

As their children grew up and produced families of their own so both Jessica and George were beginning to feel their ages. Both were over sixty and for the first time in their married lives George was slowing down on his drinking. George appeared more content to sit at home listening to their first real luxury in their lifetime, the radio, when the crystal set crackled into action, George and the rest, all fell silent. Fortunately they had enough able- bodied offspring to be able to take the batteries, an essential if the radio was to work to change. This usually took place once a fortnight. The small shop set up especially for the sale of radios and the exchange of batteries was on the corner of Cobden Street and Moor Lane. It was a walk of some fifteen minutes from their house and therefore carrying heavy batteries was not for the feint hearted.

George leant in the corner of his chair, ear near the radio, puffing on his pipe drinking his one pint of beer collected as usual from the 'Beer Off' by Jessica he was content to be close to a warm fire in the bosom of his family. Jessica looked at him and smiled, thinking of the fact that he hadn't been too bad a husband, at least he'd worked hard for his family and never played around with loose women, which was more than could be said for some husbands.

CHAPTER 50

I n 1932 Matthew returned home on leave, he was now 31 years old, and Jessica had given up hope of him ever being married. He had spent the last five years in the Holy land and Jessica had kept every tiny memento he had sent neatly filed in her Bible bag, that was a black leather handbag containing her Bible and other precious nick knacks. The bag hung on a six-inch nail hammered into the mantelpiece. Jessica had marked on the maps in the back of the Bible every place Matthew had visited.

On his return Matthew bought his Mother two special presents, one, a dark blue handkerchief with a hand painted illustration of the 'Wailing Wall' and a small flower picked when he paid a visit to the Garden of Gethsemane. He had carefully pressed the tiny flower between the pages of his own Bible to ensure it didn't get damaged during transit.

Matthew discussed with George and Jessica the worries over Germany. 'They'll never do what they did before', said George.

'Maybe Dad, maybe', said Matthew, 'but you know how

short memories are, an not many as fought in the last war would be likely to fight in the next would they?'

'The last war ended war for good, that's what's you all fought for', said George.

'Let's talk of something else son, it's high time you packed this travelling in and settled down like everybody else' said Jessica.

'Not yet Mam, I'm off to Africa in two weeks, there's too much to see', and anyway the Army's my life' said Matthew.

Lillian's husband George Trueman was an excellent provider and, in addition to his garden allotment that he gardened to perfection, he also had a small plot of land on which he kept a few pigs, chickens and rabbits. Lillian spent much of her time boiling up the potato peelings and other vegetable refuse with oats that George fed to the pigs. The family was therefore well provided for, in fact there was little to purchase apart from the basics such as tea, sugar, milk, flour and yeast.

Matthew had for the present finished with his travels and was in barracks in Leicester a mere eleven miles away. There was a regular bus service and he was now able to make regular visits to his ageing parents.

One Sunday Jessica had just mashed the tea when they heard two sets of footsteps in the entry. The gate and then the back door opened, Matthew shouted,

'Hello Mam, Dad'.

He walked in followed by a young woman, she was about twenty-five years old, fair-haired and well built, and she was tall, at least five feet nine inches,

'Mam, Dad, this is Vi", said Matthew proudly.

George puffed on his pipe and commented,

'Well I'm blowed',

Vi or Violet to be precise was well dressed and well spoken, it emerged that she, as Emily, Charlie's wife, was an only child, and her family even owned their own house.

The courtship lasted nine months before Matthew announced his forthcoming marriage. After the wedding they were to make their home in the Leicester where Vi's parents had put down the deposit on a small house in Wigston on the outskirts of the city. Within six months they announced that they were expecting a baby.

Less than a year later William announced his forthcoming marriage to Beatrice, known as Beatie and moved into a small house in Oxford Street in Loughborough.

'That just leaves two of them', said Jessica, they're both at work, an now you're not working every day we can settle down, God knows we've had it hard enough', said Jessica.

George and Jessica had been married for thirty-eight years The family decided it was high time their parents, nearing seventy, deserved a break, they saved money every week for six months, then, when everything was ready, they descended on Jessica and George en mass.

'To what do we owe this honour?' said George sitting fast in his chair in case he lost it to another, With the exception of Louise and George all were married, All those married, with the exception of Charlie and Emily had children of their own.

It was Matthew, always the confident one amongst them who spoke.

'You've looked after us all so long, we've decided to give you a holiday, we've got you tickets on the train to Skegness, and we've booked you into a good boarding house for a week, you're both going to be looked after for a week at least'.

They sat dumb founded; they had never before been on

a train, never mind even seen a city eleven miles away. They were not only going to ride on a train but were to go at least one hundred miles away from home and even see the sea.

'I don't know if my old heart will cope with all this excitement', said Jessica, almost giggling with delight.

'You've got to Mam', said Louise, 'look what a total waste of money it would be', they all laughed heartedly.

'Cheeky devil', said George laughing.

'Makes a change to be able to be cheeky, it's never happened before', said Lillian.

The great day arrived, Jessica borrowed an old suitcase from Mrs. Kent her neighbour, and she had never had need of one before. She carefully folded the newly ironed blouse and underwear and a clean shirt for George. She tidied the house, checked the pantry to ensure Louise and George junior had enough food.

At eleven O'clock all was ready, the train left at eleven thirty, and the family had added the final luxury in the holiday, they had hired a car to deliver George and Jessica to the station. The clock ticked by as they sat anxiously in the living room and Jessica announced for at least the fifth time,

'You don't think the drivers' forgot do you?'

'You don't want to be standing on that draughty railway platform for ages do you, it'll be here', George re-lit his pipe once more and began to puff away gently.

There was a sharp knock on the front door, and although Jessica was expecting it, nevertheless she leapt to her feet, as if she had heard a gunshot.

'Come on George, we'll miss the train, and we don't want to keep that driver waiting', she dashed to the door, George, rising followed slowly behind her.

Jessica stood by the car waiting for George to shut the door behind them, the neighbours had come out to see them off and Lillian came forward with a brown paper bag.

'A bit of cake to eat on the train Mam', she said thrusting it into Jessica's trembling hand, Lillian hugged her Mother and then her Father.

That'll do, that'll do,' said George. 'We're going on a holiday, not leaving the country, come on old gel, let's get you into this thing', he patted Jessica's backside as he said that, whilst the driver placed the small case inside the boot.

'Come on dearie', said the driver, helping Jessica inside the car, George followed, struggling with the narrow door, as he did so the car could be felt to sag with the weight.

Jessica sat bolt upright in the rear of the car. She sat on the edge of her seat, hat on head, coat neatly buttoned, handbag perched on her lap with her tiny hands grasping the handles of the bag as if she let it go it would escape from her possession. As the car drew off, she put her hand on her hat to hold it in place before slipping sideways, giving her a slightly tipsy look.

George, waistcoat buttoned, collar on his shirt, his heavy silver watch dangling across his large beer belly, sleeves rolled and jacket, much too small unbuttoned. On his head he wore a hat that was once described as a trilby, but the imagination needed to be stretched somewhat to see its shape now.

'Bye'

'Bye ' could be heard from numerous people all-waving enthusiastically.

The car drew up at the station; George alighted first, holding his hand out to assist his wife. Once out Jessica straightened her hat, smoothed her coat, shook her body a little and hooked her arm through George's. They made an amusing little picture, he, case in one hand, wife on other arm. She, with her bag over the other forearm, was waddling into the station.

'Come on then' she said voice full of nervous anticipation. 'In for a penny, in for a pound' and bravely marched forward to begin the second phase of their adventure.

The train drew into the station, as it did so, the noise was so deafening, the smoke choking, both jumped back.

Jessica and George made their way to the small compartment. Jessica stroked the heavy velvet material and sat down. George sat next to her, after placing the suitcase on the woven string baggage rack above their heads. After he was seated he drew down the armrest that divided their seat.

'Well, did you ever see such a thing', Jessica exclaimed, and proceeded to stroke the upholstery.

The journey continued un-eventfully and after a brief stop at Lincoln Station, where, as they entered the city, Jessica gazed in complete wonderment at the Cathedral, they drew eventually into Skegness Station.

At the station there were cars, in addition to several horse and carts waiting to take the passengers to their final destination.

'Let's get the horse and cart George, I feel much safer than in one of those mechanical contraptions', Jessica said as she stood outside the station.

George walked up to the driver, leaving Jessica standing looking around her, and suitcase at her feet. He then beckoned her towards him,

'Fetch the case then' she called, 'You're supposed to be a gent you know'.

CHAPTER 51

Once settled into the open cart, George showed the driver the slip of paper with the address of where they were to stay on it, and they set off at a gentle pace.

'Just like it should be, much better than all this rushing about', said Jessica.

Nellie Green welcomed them into the small front parlour of the terraced house; it was clean and well furnished.

'Good to see you, hope you had a good journey', she said shaking hands firstly with George, then with Jessica. We've no rules apart from we don't like our guests getting drunk an noisy, we don't mind you going for a drink, so long as it's you knowing your limits.'

Jessica nudged George, 'You listening', she said, knowing for one of the rare times in her life she had the upper hand, he wouldn't dare shame everyone. George simply nodded.

When Mrs. Green had told them the times for eating they decided to go for a stroll before tea which was to be served at 4.30pm sharp.

They were lodged only a few steps from the main road

which lead directly down to the sea front, so, arm in arm they strolled down this road to catch their very first glimpse of the sea.

Once actually on the promenade they marvelled at the pier, the lights, and the broad road that followed the sea front, of course the lights were not lit, but their imaginations were already working overtime.

'I thought the sea would be right up to the road', George said.

'So did I', said Jessica.

'Come on gel', said George, 'let's go on the beach, at least we can say we got that near to the sea, and later if we've got the energy we can walk further down the beach to the sea'.

They stepped on the sand, and George, on seeing other men, was soon down to his shirtsleeves, coat hung over his arm.

Jessica kept her hat and coat on, 'You never know what this sea air'll do to you' she declared.

They hired a couple of deck chairs, and after several attempts George managed to erect them. They relaxed in the warm sunshine, both nodding.

Suddenly Jessica gripped George's arm tightly, 'George, George, am I awake or asleep?'

'Uh' answered George.

'Are you listening George, that sea's moved, or we have it's much closer'.

George opened his eyes and sprang to his feet with more agility than he had for the past twenty years.

'Let's go for tea, an work this one out',

He bought an evening paper on the way back to their lodgings, and remembered, as he read the tide times, that the reason, of course, for the change in the sea was the tide.

The rest of the holiday passed by pleasantly, they visited the pier theatre twice, they played on the slot machines, when Jessica wasn't looking, George even ventured to look at 'What the Butler Saw', after first checking around to ensure that no one else was looking at him. They even had a drink every evening, but Jessica made sure his limited was three pints.

'Well gel', George said once again, the times he started that phrase lately, "I've seen the sand, seen the sea, bin on a train, if I die tomorrow at least I've done things I never thought I would'.

'Don't say that George', said Jessica, sounding concerned,

'It's only in the past few years you've been worth living with'.

'I don't know whether that's a compliment or not' he chuckled.

CHAPTER 52

After their journey home George and Louise, who had tea of, salmon and cucumber sandwiches, and simnel cake waiting, met them at the station.

They spent the next few weeks relating their experiences to each member of the family as they paid a visit.

By January the following year they were to become Edwardians for the second time in their lives. They had known the King's life was drawing to an end. One writer described the end:

'The sun set in a scarlet glow on January 20th 1936, and the flat fen country stretching to the west of Sandringham's wooded plateau was bathed in rich light.

Propped up in a chair facing the sunset sat King George the Fifth in Sandringham House, moving uneasily between the worlds of dream and reality.

In the next room sat the Prince of Wales, flown back from London at noon that day. Darkness fell. The rambling Mansion was hushed. The evening moved on and the dying Monarch's eyes opened fitfully. At five minutes to one in the morning by the clocks in the house, King George peacefully entered upon a glory greater than his own.'

Once again the nation was plunged into morning. As the radio announcer pronounced as many had before, 'The King is Dead, God Save the King'. A recording of the words proclaiming Edward King on January 22nd 1936 were heard, ending in 'our lawful and rightful liege Lord Edward the Eighth'.

CHAPTER 53

It was on July 1st, that George was injured, he had been sweeping up in the chain shop, when the cable to a hoist snapped, although the chain didn't actually fall, for it would certainly have killed George if it had, it swung to the ground hitting George a glancing blow on the leg and foot as it did so. He was taken to hospital whilst Wilf Smith went to tell Jessica. Two hours later George hobbled into the house on crutches.

'That's it gel', he said, 'end of my working life, I somehow don't think I'll get better in the near future'.

George's foot had not been broken, but the skin on his shin and foot had been split, and his leg and foot were now swollen and purple.

As they sat that evening listening to the radio the news was announced that a man by the name of McMohan had been arrested after throwing a loaded revolver towards the King's horse, just as he was emerging from Quadriga Arch near Hyde Park corner.

'Not again', said Jessica, 'I've not go used to King Edward

yet'.

Those next few months of their lives were spent in nursing George, his leg and foot seemed reluctant to heal, and where the breaks in the skin had occurred ulcers, which wept ceaselessly, he was constantly uncomfortable, but appeared listless in addition to this, replaced these.

After a while the newspapers began to hint about the fact that the King was seen in the company of a lady called Mrs. Simpson, not only was she an American, but also she was a married lady. At forty-two years old, the bachelor King Edward, Albert, Christian, George, Andrew, Patrick, David. Was bound to attract attention if seen in the company of a lady, but this lady was not acceptable.

The arrangements as usual were going ahead for the coronation, it was reported that on October 20th the Prime Minister visited the King, a week later Mrs. Simpson obtained a decree nisi.

In November the Prime Minister suggested that a marriage of the King to a commoner would be unacceptable. The King told Mr. Baldwin, if his marriage was not acceptable, then he would not accept the Crown of England.

The Prime Minister suggested a compromise, a morgianic marriage, whereby the King could marry Mrs. Simpson, but Mrs. Simpson could hold no title.

On Tuesday December 8th 1936, the Daily Express carried the headline, 'Mrs. Simpson Authorises, I am willing to withdraw'.

'Well, this is a right to do', said George sitting in his chair to which it seemed he was fixed for the amount of time he spent in it.

'I reckon if he can't handle it and knuckle down he should go'.

'I think she should ave stuck to one husband instead of running after our King', Jessica said as she poured the boiling water from the kettle to the teapot.

'Come on Jess, I've eard about that lad you wanted, an don't tell me there's not bin times when you wish you had'.

'What's past is past, an don't ever mention that again', said Jessica a little too quickly.

'See, you've still not forgotten him, even after all this time Jess, an you don't even know where he is, or even if he still is, anyway we're talking about the King', said George.

On December 11th 1936, the radio was tuned into the news, at 10 O'clock in the evening the Director General of the B.B.C., Sir John Reith announced.

'This is Windsor Castle, His royal Highness Prince Edward',

After a pause Edward spoke before he began his speech George took his pipe from his mouth, and said,

'That's it then, he chose her'.

'How do you know he's not talking yet', said Jessica.

They said Prince Edward' announced George.

He was of course correct, and in his 537-word speech the King abdicated.

CHAPTER 54

I t was shortly after Christmas, that George's health worsened, he hadn't been well for a good deal of time, his leg
and foot ached continually, and the doctor was called in.

The doctor told Jessica in no uncertain terms that George's
heart was considerably weaker, and that he would be asking
the Queens nurse to call at least once a week to bathe and
dress his leg and foot, as he was most concerned at the lack
of response to treatment.

It was a fine day on May 12th 1937, both Jessica and
George sat before the radio listening to the pageant being
related to them, as the King left the abbey, Jessica took up
the bottle of sherry, this had been purchased especially for
the occasion, she poured a glass for each of them and toasted
King George VI.

'God Bless Him', they chorused.

As a present for their parents the family bought various
memorabilia, mugs, books and a headscarf for Jessica, which
was neatly folded, re-wrapped and placed in the drawer.

There was a huge street party, everyone bought out either

tables or chairs, decorated the outside of their houses, the men passing bunting from one bedroom window across the street to the other. Tables were laden with fruit, cake, sandwiches; party hats were worn and presents given to the children.

CHAPTER 55

Nineteen thirty eight arrived, there was increasing concern over the man who was making his name known in Germany. His name was Heir Adolf Hitler, an Austrian who had fought in the 1st World War.

George and Jessica discussed the problems at length during that year, the word was not good.

In March Austria became part of the German Reich and in September, Neville Chamberlain the Prime Minister flew to meet Mr. Hitler. On his return stated that he was convinced it would be 'Peace in Our Time'.

The family as families over the country breathed a sigh of relief. Flo, who had been courting a young man who had been called into the army, was therefore sure of a short enlistment. Just a week before Flo and Raymond Eric Wilfred Dawkins were to be married, Hitler and Mussolini of Italy made a pact, bringing further concern.

Jessica was worried, first her daughter loses a husband, and surely to God her granddaughter could not suffer the same fate.

On September 1st 1939, Germany invaded Poland. Chamberlain sent an ultimatum to Hitler, either abandon the march on Poland, or suffer the consequences of Britain being at war. The ultimatum was to end by 11am on the morning of 3rd September.

The threat was not withdrawn and Great Britain was at war with Germany. Eric was called to his unit, just two weeks before Flo's first baby was born on October 31st, it was a boy, once again there was to be a George, they called him George, Eric, Wilfred, Wilfred after his paternal grandfather.

It was shortly after his birth that baby George developed severe eczema, after which he had breathing problems diagnosed as asthma.

While Jessica was helping Flo to care for the baby, there was a knock at the door. Louise, who was by now twenty-seven years old, ran down the stairs saying she would answer it. She was too late; George Collins had hobbled to the door and opened it to find a young man in Army uniform.

'Yes', said George.

'Could I see Louise please?' the handsome young man asked.

'What for?' enquired George.

'We've been seeing each other for a while and I've had my posting, could I see her before I leave?' he asked.

George was furious, Louise was his youngest daughter, and she was expected to stay at home to look after her ageing parents, not be thinking of courtship and marriage.

'No, you can't', George said, 'off, and never try to see her again'.

The young man went, but as he left the door he shouted, 'I love you Louise, I'll get a message to you somehow'.

Louise was distraught, she loved John Loweness dearly, she

never wanted to part from him. Her father shouted and went to strike her with his stick, she actually caught the stick and twisted it out of his hand; he clutched the doorframe to prevent himself falling over.

'I hate you, you wicked old man, I'll never forgive you for this', she ran upstairs.

After this incident George's health declined further, Louise ignored him most of the time, and the nurse was now calling every day.

The room in which Jessica and George slept had developed a strange smell over the last few days, and it seemed worse when Jessica threw the covers back on the bed each morning.

'You sure there's no dead mouse in this room?' George asked concerned.

'No there's not, but I can smell it too, like rotting meat, it's a real stink', Jessica said.

George pulled himself up to sitting, and carefully pulled his legs out of the bed,

'I wish this damned leg and foot would heal, just look at these bandages, damn things been weeping all night, that nurse will have the devil of a job getting these bindings off when she comes'.

He got up, pulled on his trousers and shirt, eventually made his way into the living room. The front room having been made into a bedroom, in order to alleviate the necessity of climbing the stairs.

When the nurse arrived, she asked Jessica for the usual bowl of water, but this time she had to thoroughly soak the bandages before she could lift them. The putrid pus had sealed them tightly together.

When she had taken the bandages from him, she gently

placed the foot in disinfected water, it was then as they all looked, and the real horror became evident.

The toes on George's foot and a good part of the foot itself had turned black, the open sores from the discarded bandages was totally unacceptable. Jessica quickly collected a newspaper and placed the filthy mess into it, wrapped it tightly, and carried it outside to the dustbin.

When she returned, she moved to George's side, and took hold of his hand. The nurse drew up a chair, and sat before them.

'I can't keep this from you Mr. and Mrs. Collins', she said, 'I'm afraid it looks and smells like gangrene, I'll call in at the doctor when I've dressed your leg and ask him to come and confirm it.'

'Thank you nurse', said Jessica.

When the nurse had finished and Jessica was showing her to the door she asked,

'Is there any hope?'

'There's always hope Mrs. Collins', said the nurse as she stepped out of the house.

'I'll go and see the doctor now'.

At three-thirty in the afternoon the doctor arrived. George was sitting on the sofa with his leg up. The baby was crying loudly. The radio speaking away and Jessica was raking the fire. He needed to knock twice before he could make himself heard. Quickly Jessica replaced the poker and turned off the radio, whilst Flo lifted the baby and went upstairs.

The doctor was shown into the room by Jessica, he examined George carefully. When the examination was over he sat on the sofa and said that he was very sorry, but the only way to cure George was to amputate the leg, high up.

George knew this was his only chance, he'd heard about

too many before him with this complaint.

The doctor hadn't mentioned the fact that he'd seen trace marks of the veins being infected and that more than likely included the blood stream. He also knew that at the age George was he would be unlikely to survive the operation. George had only a few days left on this earth.

As he left the house Jessica touched his arm, he looked at her and gently shook his head in silent affirmation of what Jessica already knew.

Jessica gave George a spoonful of the sleeping draught that the doctor had prepared, and although he seemed to be sleeping he was hot, with such a high temperature that Jessica could no longer stand the discomfort of being beside him in bed.

The next morning George drifted in and out of lucidity, not able to rise from his bed. When the doctor arrived that tiny red snake which heralded his demise was gradually working its way further up his body.

George was one minute asleep, the next shouting and raving like a mad man, and only what seemed a moment later, so calm and sensible it seemed to the family that a different man was continually inhabiting his body. The times he was awake became shorter, the times semi-comatose longer as the day progressed. By nine in the evening he was lying propped up on cushions stating that he was feeling much better, and that the pain had disappeared.

Flo brought the baby up for his great grandfather to see, he kissed the sickly baby boy, held Flo's hand and said,

'Don't worry love he'll soon be with me to look after for ever'.

George Collins junior took the day off his work; he now worked on the nearby local farm, an occupation that protected him from the need to join the armed services. He went to call on each of the family in turn to give them news of the deterioration of their father, and then went to the local post office to dictate a telegram to Matthew. The next day found George lying in bed, slipping into a coma, the family called to visit, and one by one joined their siblings in the small living room to wait for the rapidly approaching end. Lillian busied herself making sandwiches and tea by the ever-increasing cup full.

By three pm, on the Saturday afternoon of March 12th 1939 George died.

Jessica came slowly out of their bedroom; she looked around the room at her family and simply said,

'He's gone'.

She sat in her chair, Lillian handed her a cup of tea, and she took a sip. Jessica had done her crying before George's death, there was no need for more tears. After forty-two years of living with and sharing a bed, she felt totally alone.

CHAPTER 56

The funeral took place three days after George had died; it was a cold, but fine day. Jessica had trouble actually walking that day; her rheumatics were giving her some pain. She struggled into the car following the hearse and the funeral took place firstly at the local Baptist Church in Kings Street, it then progressed to the Cemetery on the outskirts of the town.

Jessica looked at the grave and smiled,

'I'll be joining you again soon George, I don't think I can sleep alone for long'.

She knew the family had bought a double plot she was therefore confident she would join him in death.

It was only six weeks after George had died that the baby was unwell. The doctor called regularly he eventually suggested that baby George be taken into hospital. They could perhaps regulate his temperature and breathing there.

Flo and Eric visited their tiny son everyday, but the improvement was not noticed. Flo complained that there was an open window near the cot that she thought was not conducive to the baby's health.

By the beginning of April, baby George took a turn for the worse, he developed pneumonia, he rapidly deteriorated and by mid April the baby died.

Eric and Flo were distraught, Jessica reflected on George's words. Was it possible that George really knew? Did he just hope he was not going to be alone? Whichever way it was, the baby did not survive, however, he chances were slim.

The baby was buried alongside his great grandfather.

CHAPTER 57

Christmas 1940 was a quiet affair. Eric was away stationed in York. Flo was hoping he would never have to fight, however, on Boxing Day he arrived home on a forty-eight hour leave; he had a posting and was to catch a train for Dover at the end of his leave.

When Eric arrived in Dover he was once again re-routed to the East coast to work in the pay office.

It was on the 2nd January that there was a knock on the door. Jessica answered the door. It was a young girl, tears streaming down her face.

'I've come to tell', she then burst once more into tears.

'Come in love', Jessica said, putting an arm around her shoulders and ushering the girl inside,

'Tell me your problem when we're inside, I'll put the kettle on'.

It took a while for the girl to calm down after she had composed herself she began.

'It's my brother John; he'd been seeing your Louise you know. We don't know what happened when they fell out, but

219

he went off in a right state. This morning we got a telegram, Oh, Mrs. Collins, he's been killed, he's never hurt anybody, an well, he loved Louise so much, we thought she ought to know,' with that she burst once more into tears.

Jessica did not know how she was going to break the news to her daughter, she knew that Louise could see no obstacle in the way to her marrying John, now that George had gone.

Jessica waited for Louise to come home, the closer to her arriving home from work the more agitated she became.

When at last Louise came into the house, Jessica, put her arm around her daughter, but said nothing. Louise looked at her mother,

'It's John, Mam isn't it, it's John.

Jessica nodded, 'Yes Love'.

'How badly injured is he Mam, it doesn't matter you know. I'll still love him, it doesn't matter what he looks like'.

'It's worse love' said Jessica fighting back the tears.

Only two daughters she'd produced both had lost the men they loved, both in wars how cruel a place this world is, thought Jessica.

Louise dissolved into floods of tears, the two women, young and old stood together in their grief, the young and old alike heartbroken. One for her love, the other for the un-dying love a mother has for her daughter, who, try as she might, she could never console. A bruised and cut knee as a child, yes, bereavement as a woman, she was helpless to cure, she could only be there to comfort.

In mid May 1940, Eric was home once more, once more there was a posting to who knew where, but they both knew it was a boat somewhere.

At the end of May the news of the British retreat was filter-ing through to those at home. The family held their breath.

Jessica prayed the women in her family were suffering again, this time it was her granddaughter whose love was on the front line.

Jessica assured Flo that no news was good news. June 3rd arrived; all day the radio announced continually, the progress of the numerous small boats crossing the channel to collect our forces from the beaches of Dunkirk.

It was the end of July, the family had still heard no news of Eric, until one Friday afternoon, as Flo left the factory where she had returned to work after the death of their baby Eric ran behind her and said 'BOO'.

Flo screamed, turned and threw her arms around his neck, when she had recovered they walked home arm in arm while Eric told her how he had boarded the boat to cross the channel on May 28th, just as Dunkirk fell, and how three hours later had disembarked whilst the boat, empty of its passengers went over the channel to bring back its beleaguered army.

Eric returned once more to his unit, and life returned to as near as normal as possible.

Louise met a man ten years her senior, who was working on the land. This time, she thought, I'll marry, but he'll be safe. Louise married Frank Brown-Ely; in the little church only a few streets from where she had spent her whole life. By May 28th the following year she had produced a son whom she called Michael.

In June, the situation was worsening in Europe, with the invasion of Russia by Germany, whilst Britain braced itself for an invasion, which now seemed more possible than ever.

In July, Flo gave birth to a daughter, she couldn't face this prospect, and she had convinced herself her beloved son would be re-born. A girl was the last thing she wanted, she had not even thought of a name for the child. Eric was given leave and arrived home to see his daughter, she was no beauty and they both reflected their disappointment when they looked at their child.

'Go and register her', said Flo.

'what do you want to call it, um, her?' asked Eric.

'Oh, Janet, that'll do', said Flo taking little interest in the matter.

Eric went to the registry office. By the time he reached there he had forgotten the name. The name Joan sprang to mind, it wasn't what had been intended, but it would do, he called the child Joan Margaret.

By December 7th, the situation was once again worsening, when Japan bombed Pearl Harbour and by the December 8th 1941 Britain and the United States were at war with Japan. As a boost to moral just before Christmas 1941, the United States declared war on Germany and Italy.

The war progressed, Jessica followed each step avidly on the radio, the family were worried by knew there was little they could do about it.

CHAPTER 58

There were things that Joan loved and remembered clearly about being brought up by Jessica. Jessica made such wonderful chocolate truffles, these were made using dried milk and of course cocoa powder, but how they were put together will only be conjecture now.

The thing she loved doing was to sit, in the evening close to Jessica and to be allowed to take down that little black bag from its' nail. She would very gently remove the blue silk handkerchief and the small now fragile flower and always to ask the same questions. How and why?

George Trueman was the most magnificent grandfather to the little girl. He would take simple tins and manufacture them into toys, trains, cars, and carts. All done at the local factory given over to the manufacture of armaments. As so many men at the factory did work for the home, these were called 'Government jobs', meaning top secret not allowed to discuss, should anyone ask what was being done.

George still kept pigs, now illegal if they were not registered and they were not registered. He would go to visit neighbours not merely for social activities but because they would save potato peelings and vegetables, these were put in the small truck that he pushed. Joan always holding onto the handle of the truck when she was allowed to go with him, when he returned Lillian would have cleaned the copper used for boiling the washing and tipped in some oats and water, the fire under the copper would have been lit and the whole lot be coming to the boil as George Trueman came through the gate with the vegetables. The vegetables would then be tipped into the mixture and the lot well cooked before being put into pails and taken to feed the pigs.

When autumn came at least one pig would be killed. The family had the job of salting the meat before hanging it on hooks on the stairs to cure. Many neighbours had very good dinners throughout the war thanks to George Trueman risking imprisonment to feed them.

By 1943 and 44, Jessica was taking the tiny girl outside each time she heard the bombers overhead, and allowing her to watch the search lights used to protect the town.

On 7th May 1945, General Jodi made an unconditional surrender of Germany, the whole nation was relieved, there was dancing and singing in the streets, and a general state of euphoria existed, not only in the family, but also over the whole land.

Jessica was happy to provide some food for the party that was once again organised in the street. They celebrated as they had done before, the large Union Jack was placed outside the bedroom window and the window closed on the pole. The men assisted in decorating the street. The people felt they could once again relax.

Although Jessica did not attend the party, she watched the merry making from her window. She was by now feeling her age, she just could not bring herself to be entertained in this way any longer.

By August 10th, news was filtering through about the Americans dropping a new kind of bomb on Japan, unbelievable numbers of people were killed in the most terrible way. Jessica, along with a great many other people were appalled at this destruction, but if the Americans entering the war and dropping the bomb meant an end to World War 11, then they supposed it must be worth it, but why kill so many innocent people in the process?

When the capitulation of Japan occurred it was once again time for celebration, Joan as with a great many other children attended fancy dress parties, all of which included marching down the roads. Joan marched in Leicester Road, she went to a party at the Cross Keys pub that was one of the places George Trueman drank in. That V.J. (Victory over Japan) party was the culmination of attempting to keep children whose parents had been split by that terrible war, happy. The children had grown up imitating the marching soldiers whose presence always seemed to be around.

Jessica got her enjoyment of the event when Joan returned home full of excitement as befits a five-year-old child, and told her great granny all that had happened that day.

As every day came Jessica became more tired, she went to bed early, and when Lillian called next door to visit her mother in the afternoons, she sometimes found her mother resting on the bed, a thing she had never been known to do before.

Jessica had a small broach in the shape of a donkey, she had never been known to wear this broach. Joan was allowed to look at it if she had been especially good. There had, of course, been talk of Jessica's deteriorating condition and Joan was always alert to words around her. Although not under-standing the fact that the person who had cared for her was soon no longer was ever watchful. One day, as Joan was sit-ting on Jessica's knee she asked,

'Granny, when you die, can I have the donkey?'

'When I die', said Jessica.

CHAPTER 59

During the spring of 1947, the news came that Emma, Jessica's sister had died. Jessica, knew, that like herself she had been unwell for sometime, and asked Flo to call and buy a wreath, and have it delivered to Emma's house. Jessica herself was far too weak to go to her sister's funeral, as she was just getting over a chest infection.

Shortly afterwards Eric was demobilised from the Army, but he was not well. He and Flo still lived at Jessica's house. Jessica and her youngest son George were kept awake most nights by Eric's continual coughing.

As the months wore on Eric's cough grew worse. When he now had a bout of coughing, he would cough up a great deal of blood.

Eric eventually went to the doctor who diagnosed the advanced stages of tuberculosis. Eric must have contracted the disease in the Army, but too much time had passed for proof, he was therefore unable to claim a disability pension. Flo in the meantime worked hard to keep the flow of money into the household.

Jessica worried about Eric's illness. She had seen the disease spread through and wipe out whole families in a very short time, she therefore made every attempt to keep Joan's contact with her father to an absolute minimum.

Eric grew worse, unable to walk only a short distance before he was finding the need to sit down and rest. Eventually he was admitted to the nearby sanatorium at Markfield. Jessica was once again worried that her granddaughter was very close to losing her husband.

Eric's condition was now one of touch and go, operations to remove lungs had been performed before, but no one had survived more than a few weeks.

Flo was called into the surgeon's room when she went to visit Eric. He was in a very cold room, as it was thought at that time that fresh air helped to alleviate the symptoms.

The rooms sometimes held two patients there were French windows, which were open all day, every day no matter what the weather.

Mr. Brown stood up as Flo entered, and shook hands,

'Please sit down Mrs. Dawkins', he said offering her a seat before the large desk, as he once again settled himself in his chair. He discussed the seriousness of her husband's condition and also the treatment he wished to undertake. Flo could only nod, she knew the situation held little prospect of success.

Eric transferred after six months to another hospital called Groby Hospital where the operation was to be performed. On Friday, the operation was performed, and Jessica could be seen holding her Bible close to her heart, eyes closed in her chair. The operation took six hours and Eric had survived the initial procedure. When Flo visited him he was still unconscious but seemed to be breathing soundly. Mr. Brown assured her that her husband was a strong young man and if anyone could survive such a trauma it would be Eric.

In the early hours of Sunday morning a loud knocking could be heard and a motorcar engine running. Flo flung open the bedroom window and looked out. It was a young policeman, 'Mrs. Dawkins"?

'Yes', said Flo, heart racing.

'Mrs. Dawkins', called the policeman, could you get dressed and come with me. I'm afraid your husband's taken a turn for the worse love, and the hospital would like you there as soon as possible'.

Flo didn't answer, she closed the window gently and hands trembling began to get dressed.

When Flo arrived at the hospital, Mr. Brown, who had been called, met her.

'I'm afraid we look like losing him dear' he said, 'you see, he was just regaining consciousness, and it appears he spotted an orange on his bedside table and reach across for it, he's split the wound dear, and lost a good deal of blood'. Flo, looked at the surgeon not able to speak or cry, too devastated by the news.

Flo stayed by Eric's side all night, and the Police brought her back home to her little daughter and grandmother at nine O'clock the following morning. Eric, although not out of danger had survived the crisis.

'Off to bed gel', said Jessica, 'get some rest, you'll need it over the next few weeks'.

Eric spent a further six months in hospital after his operation and although weak was sent home with an expected life span of a further five years.

CHAPTER 60

Jessica, was now visibly weakening, each day that passed was becoming more difficult, her breathing was difficult and her face pale and drawn.

During the spring of 1949 she could no longer get out of bed, the family visited her regularly, but she, and they knew, she would never rise again from her bed.

On Monday afternoon breathing became so difficult she was having trouble speaking, again, as with George's end, her family were gathered in the living room.

Lillian had gone into her mother and was sitting, support-ing her, with halting breath Jessica asked for Joan. The little girl came to her great grandmother's bedside. Jessica fought to control her breathing so as not to alarm the child. She took hold of the child's hand and placed the donkey into it. There was no need for words, Joan knew she was never to see Jessica again. Jessica simply relaxed onto her pillow, and smiled at the child.